My Life and Hard Times and Other Observations

James Thurber

Selected and with
an introduction by
Tim Wilkinson

THE FOLIO SOCIETY
London 1980

This edition is published by kind permission of Hamish Hamilton Ltd, London and Harper & Row Publications Ltd, New York.

PHOTOTYPESET IN 10 POINT V.I.P. OPTIMA SPACED 2 POINTS
BY WESTERN PRINTING SERVICES LTD, BRISTOL
PRINTED BY W & J MACKAY LTD, CHATHAM
ON GUARD BRIDGE FINE BOOK WOVE PAPER
BOUND BY W & J MACKAY LTD
USING REDBRIDGE BUCKRAM CLOTH
AND BLOCKED WITH A DRAWING
BY THE AUTHOR

Printed in Great Britain

Contents

Introduction

This selection presents what I think is Thurber at his best. I have tried to make it representative of every period in his writing life – except for what always used to be known as *juvenilia*. It does *not* include any straight journalism or, except in 'The Lady on the Bookcase', any pictorial jokes. In these categories I am sad to have left out 'Soapland', a series of articles describing in vivid terms the world of the daytime radio soap-operas, and *The Last Flower*, a picture book with minimal captions depicting the fall and rise of civilisation – wonderfully hopeful considering its year of publication, 1939.

I have not attempted to date the stories but I have put them in order of their publication in collections. The titles and dates of the collections themselves are included in the Contents and there is, therefore, reasonable assurance that the order in this book represents roughly the order of composition. I have reprinted only those drawings which were included in the collections made before Thurber died in 1961.

The impression of the writer which one get from the stories seems largely to suggest Thurber as he really was. His bad eyesight, which prompts many of his funniest situations, stemmed from his loss of an eye as a child of six, accidentally shot with an arrow by his brother while playing at William Tell. In 1940, at the age of forty-six, he suffered five operations on the remaining eye and was left with only minimum vision: he was practically blind for the last fourteen years of his life. He died in 1961 shortly before his sixty-seventh birthday. The great influences in his life were Harold Ross, who hired Thurber in 1927 as an editor, and later as a writer, for the *New Yorker*, and E. B. (Andy) White with whom Thurber shared an office at the *New Yorker*. Thurber's first success was the skit on psychiatry which he and White wrote together *Is Sex Necessary?* and which became a best-seller on publication in 1929. Ross died in 1952 and in 1958 Thurber published the controversial *The Years with Ross* which seems to have caused his estrangement from most of his old *New Yorker* colleagues.

It is amusing to contrast the two major films made from Thurber's work. *The Secret Life of Walter Mitty* made by Samuel

Goldwyn in 1947 was a wonderful vehicle for Danny Kaye's idiosyncratic abilities – but it was a travesty of the original story. On the other hand *The Battle of the Sexes*, a British film starring Peter Sellers, Constance Cummings and Robert Morley, happily translated the plot of 'The Catbird Seat' into an old-fashioned Scotch firm without losing the feeling of the original.

Thurber himself was always attracted to the theatre, in his early days writing the 'book' for many amateur musical shows. In 1939 he collaborated with his old college friend Elliot Nugent in a play called *The Male Animal*. First produced in Los Angeles it became a Broadway hit in 1940 and was revived in New York in 1951. In 1960 his most famous and probably best collection *A Thurber Carnival* was turned into a revue in which, in spite of his blindness, he appeared himself.

It is always difficult to think of an author who died so recently as Thurber as a 'classic'. But in the true definition of a classic as something which can never again be surpassed many of Thurber's pieces pass with no reservations. As soon as one starts to read the stories one is in what can only be, at the same time, a unique Thurber world and a universal one which we all share. Nobody is able as he is to raise the minor embarassments of modern life almost to the level of tragedy – and then discharge the resultant tension in fits of laughter. Some of his phrases have even passed into common usage. How many of us have used ourselves, or wryly observed our host using, at a dinner party his immortal disclaimer, originally a caption to a drawing 'It's a naïve domestic Burgundy but I think you'll be amused by its presumption' without proper acknowledgement?

There is always a nagging feeling that humorous writing is not quite as important as serious writing, that stories which make one laugh cannot be as great art as stories that make one cry. In human terms this is clearly nonsense: we read fiction to be amused and to be transported elsewhere – into a cleaner, brighter world than the one we live in. This is refreshing: it allows us to come back to our familiar and time-worn world with a new eye and with a better appreciation of the virtues we have come to take for granted. For this purpose humour is often the readiest catalyst because in itself it often relies upon the device of turning the familiar upside-down into the preposterous, and I think we often value funny writing too lightly just because it makes us laugh. Nevertheless I am glad to include here two late stories which show what Thurber might have produced had he turned to 'serious' writing.

In one way, of course, Thurber was deadly serious and that was in his precise use of language. He really cared about how something was said and took immense pains that the construction of his sentences conveyed exactly what he meant in the most telling way. Behind his practical jokes and word-games lay a real love of the words themselves, their overtones and associations, and their ability to conjure up images. Robert Louis Stevenson's dictum 'easy reading, hard writing' applies with the greatest force to the magazine story writer: he is competing for attention against other and maybe more fashionable articles so that he must grab the reader's attention at the outset and hold it to the end. Thurber seems to achieve this so effortlessly that one can only guess at the immense pains he must have taken to get it right.

On the other hand such writing is very dense and concentrated, and is inclined to cause mental indigestion if taken in large doses. I very nearly turned away from the work myself when I was reading everything by Thurber I could find before making my selection. It is a measure of his skill that after a suitable delay I am now able to enjoy him as much as I ever have — perhaps even more.

A last word needs to be said about spelling. It is well-known that Americans prefer color and theater and catalog and smolder and plow and skeptical to English colour, theatre, catalogue, smoulder, plough and sceptical, but what about curb/kerb which appears in a story title? To an English eye curb has a different meaning to kerb in spite of the ultimate derivation. Thurber is a peculiarly American writer; even when he is writing about France he retains his pronounced national attitude, and it would seem unfair to anglicise him. His English publishers, Hamish Hamilton have always done so and we, also English but with a large American membership, have decided to follow suit. This is the place to apologise to all those readers who think we are wrong: I like to think there would be no need to apologise to the author himself who would have been the first to appreciate the irony.

TIM WILKINSON

Preface to a Life

Benvenuto Cellini said that a man should be at least forty years old before he undertakes so fine an enterprise as that of setting down the story of his life. He said also that an autobiographer should have accomplished something of excellence. Nowadays nobody who has a typewriter pays any attention to the old master's quaint rules. I myself have accomplished nothing of excellence except a remarkable and, to some of my friends, unaccountable expertness in hitting empty ginger ale bottles with small rocks at a distance of thirty paces. Moreover, I am not yet forty years old. But the grim date moves toward me apace; my legs are beginning to go, things blur before my eyes, and the faces of the rose-lipped maids I knew in my twenties are misty as dreams.

At forty my faculties may have closed up like flowers at evening, leaving me unable to write my memoirs with a fitting and discreet inaccuracy or, having written them, unable to carry them to the publisher's. A writer verging into the middle years lives in dread of losing his way to the publishing house and wandering down to the Bowery or the Battery, there to disappear like Ambrose Bierce. He has sometimes also the kindred dread of turning a sudden corner and meeting himself sauntering along in the opposite direction. I have known writers at this dangerous and tricky age to phone their homes from their offices, or their offices from their homes, ask for themselves in a low tone, and then, having fortunately discovered that they were 'out', to collapse in hard-breathing relief. This is particularly true of writers of light pieces running from a thousand to two thousand words.

The notion that such persons are gay of heart and carefree is curiously untrue. They lead, as a matter of fact, an existence of jumpiness and apprehension. They sit on the edge of the chair of Literature. In the house of Life they have the feeling that they have never taken off their overcoats. Afraid of losing themselves in the larger flight of the two-volume novel, or even the one-volume novel, they stick to short accounts of their misadventures because they never get so deep into them but that they feel they can get out.

This type of writing is not a joyous form of self-expression but the manifestation of a twitchiness at once cosmic and mundane. Authors of such pieces have, nobody knows why, a genius for getting into minor difficulties: they walk into the wrong apartments, they drink furniture polish for stomach bitters, they drive their cars into the prize tulip beds of haughty neighbours, they playfully slap gangsters, mistaking them for old school friends. To call such persons 'humorists', a loose-fitting and ugly word, is to miss the nature of their dilemma and the dilemma of their nature. The little wheels of their invention are set in motion by the damp hand of melancholy.

Such a writer moves about restlessly wherever he goes, ready to get the hell out at the drop of a pie-pan or the lift of a skirt. His gestures are the ludicrous reflexes of the maladjusted; his repose is the momentary inertia of the nonplussed. He pulls the blinds against the morning and creeps into smokey corners at night. He talks largely about small matters and smally about great affairs. His ears are shut to the ominous rumblings of the dynasties of the world moving toward a cloudier chaos than ever before, but he hears with an acute perception the startling sounds that rabbits make twisting in the bushes along a country road at night and a cold chill comes upon him when the comic supplement of a Sunday newspaper blows unexpectedly out of an areaway and envelopes his knees. He can sleep while the commonwealth crumbles but a strange sound in the pantry at three in the morning will strike terror into his stomach. He is not afraid, or much aware, of the menaces of empire but he keeps looking behind him as he walks along darkening streets out of the fear that he is being softly followed by little men padding along in single file, about a foot and half high, large-eyed, and whiskered.

It is difficult for such a person to conform to what Ford Madox Ford in his book of recollections has called the sole reason for writing one's memoirs: namely, to paint a picture of one's time. Your short-piece writer's time is not Walter Lippmann's time, or Stuart Chase's time, or Professor Einstein's time. It is his own personal time, circumscribed by the short boundaries of his pain and his embarrassment, in which what happens to his digestion, the rear axle of his car, and the confused flow of his relationships with six or eight persons and two or three buildings is of greater importance than what goes on in the nation or in the universe. He knows vaguely that the nation is not much good any more; he has read that the crust of the earth is shrinking alarmingly and that the universe is growing steadily colder, but he does not believe that any of the three is in half as bad shape as he is.

Enormous strides are made in star-measurement, theoretical economics, and the manufacture of bombing planes, but he usually doesn't find out about them until he picks up an old copy of 'Time' on a picnic grounds or in the summer house of a friend. He is aware that billions of dollars are stolen every year by bankers and politicians, and that thousands of people are out of work, but these conditions do not worry him a tenth as much as the conviction that he has wasted three months on a stupid psychoanalyst or the suspicion that a piece he has been working on for two long days was done much better and probably more quickly by Robert Benchley in 1924.

The 'time' of such a writer, then, is hardly worth reading about if the reader wishes to find out what was going on in the world while the writer in question was alive and at what might be laughingly called 'his best'. All that the reader is going to find out is what happened to the writer. The compensation, I suppose, must lie in the comforting feeling that one has had, after all, a pretty sensible and peaceful life, by comparison. It is unfortunate, however, that even a well-ordered life cannot lead anybody safely around the inevitable doom that waits in the skies. As F. Hopkinson Smith long ago pointed out, the claw of the sea-puss gets us all in the end.

J.T.

Sandy Hook,
Connecticut,
25 September 1933.

The Night the Bed Fell

I suppose that the high-water mark of my youth in Columbus, Ohio, was the night the bed fell on my father. It makes a better recitation (unless, as some friends of mine have said, one has heard it five or six times) than it does a piece of writing, for it is almost necessary to throw furniture around, shake doors, and bark like a dog, to lend the proper atmosphere and verisimilitude to what is admittedly a somewhat incredible tale. Still, it did take place.

It happened, then, that my father had decided to sleep in the attic one night, to be away where he could think. My mother opposed the notion strongly because, she said, the old wooden bed up there was unsafe; it was wobbly and the heavy headboard would crash down on father's head in case the bed fell, and kill him. There was no dissuading him, however, and at a quarter past ten he closed the attic door behind him and went up the narrow twisting stairs. We later heard ominous creakings as he crawled into bed. Grandfather, who usually slept in the attic bed when he was with us, had disappeared some days before. (On these occasions he was usually gone six or eight days and returned growling and out of temper, with the news that the federal Union was run by a passel of blockheads and that the Army of the Potomac didn't have any more chance than a fiddler's bitch.)

We had visiting us at this time a nervous first cousin of mine named Briggs Beall, who believed that he was likely to cease breathing when he was asleep. It was his feeling that if he were not awakened every hour during the night, he might die of suffocation. He had been accustomed to setting an alarm clock to ring at intervals until morning, but I persuaded him to abandon this. He slept in my room and I told him that I was such a light sleeper that if anybody quit breathing in the same room with me, I would wake instantly. He tested me the first night – which I had suspected he would – by holding his breath after my regular breathing had convinced him I was asleep. I was not asleep, however, and called to him. This seemed to allay his fears a little, but he took the precaution of putting a glass of spirits of camphor on a little table at the head of his bed. In case I didn't arouse him until he was almost gone, he said, he would sniff the camphor, a powerful reviver. Briggs was not the only member of his family who had his crotchets. Old Aunt Melissa Beall (who could whistle like a man, with two fingers in her mouth) suffered under the premonition that she was destined to die on South High Street, because she had been born on South High Street and married on South High Street. Then there was Aunt Sarah Shoaf, who never went to bed at night without the fear that a burgular was going to get in and blow chloroform under her door through a tube. To avert this calamity – for she was in greater dread of anesthetics than of losing her household goods – she always piled her money, silverware, and other valuables in a neat stack just outside her bedroom, with a note reading: 'This is all I have. Please take it and do not use your chloroform, as this is all I have'. Aunt Gracie Shoaf also had a burglar phobia, but she met it with more fortitude. She was confident that burglars had been getting into her house every night for forty years. The fact that she never missed anything was to her no proof to the contrary. She always claimed that she scared them off · before they could take anything, by throwing shoes down the hallway. When she went to bed she piled, where she could get at them handily, all the shoes there were about her house. Five minutes after she had turned off the light, she would sit up in bed and say 'Hark'! Her husband, who had learned to ignore the whole situation as long ago as 1903, would either be sound asleep or pretend to be sound asleep. In either case he would not respond to her tugging and pulling, so that presently she would arise, tiptoe to the door, open it slightly and heave a shoe down the hall in one direction, and its mate down the hall in the other direction. Some nights she threw them all, some nights only a couple of pair.

But I am straying from the remarkable incidents that took place during the night that the bed fell on father. By midnight we were all in bed. The layout of the rooms and the disposition of their occupants is important to an understanding of what later occurred. In the front room upstairs (just under father's attic bedroom) were my mother and my brother Herman, who sometimes sang in his sleep, usually 'Marching Through Georgia' or 'Onward, Christian Soldiers'. Briggs Beall and myself were in a room adjoining this one. My brother Roy was in a room across the hall from ours. Our bull terrier, Rex, slept in the hall.

My bed was an army cot, one of those affairs which are made wide enough to sleep on comfortably only by putting up, flat with the middle section, the two sides which ordinarily hang down like

Some nights she threw them all

the sideboards of a drop-leaf table. When these sides are up, it is perilous to roll to far toward the edge, for then the cot is likely to tip completely over, bringing the whole bed down on top of one, with a tremendous banging crash. This, in fact, is precisely what happened, about two o'clock in the morning. (It was my mother who, in recalling the scene later, first referred to it as 'the night the bed fell on your father'.)

Always a deep sleeper, slow to arouse (I had lied to Briggs), I was at first unconscious of what had happened when the iron cot rolled me onto the floor and toppled over on me. It left me still warmly bundled up and unhurt, for the bed rested above me like a canopy. Hence I did not wake up, only reached the edge of consciousness and went back. The racket, however, instantly awakened my mother, in the next room, who came to the immediate conclusion that her worst dread was realised: the big wooden bed upstairs had fallen on father. She therefore screamed, 'Let's go to your poor father!' It was this shout, rather than the noise of my cot falling, that awakened Herman, in the same room with her. He thought that mother had become, for no apparent reason, hysterical.' 'You're all right, Mamma!' he shouted, trying to calm her. They exchanged shout for shout for perhaps ten seconds: 'Let's go to your poor father!' and 'You're all right!' That woke up Briggs. By this time I was conscious of what was going on, in a vague way, but did not yet realise that I was under my bed instead of on it. Briggs, awakening in the midst of loud shouts of fear and apprehension, came to the quick conclusion that he was suffocating and that we were all trying to 'bring him out'. With a low moan, he grasped the glass of camphor at the head of his bed and instead of sniffing it poured it over himself. The room reeked of camphor. 'Ugf, ahfg', choked Briggs, like a drowning man, for he had almost succeeded in stopping his breath under the deluge of pungent spirits. He leaped out of bed and groped toward the open window, but he came up against one that was closed. With his hand, he beat out the glass, and I could hear it crash and tinkle on the alleyway below. It was at this juncture that I, in trying to get up, had the uncanny sensation of feeling my bed above me! Foggy with sleep, I now suspected, in my turn, that the whole uproar was being made in a frantic endeavor to extricate me from what must be an unheard-of and perilous situation. 'Get me out of this!' I bawled. 'Get me out!' I think I had the nightmarish belief that I was entombed in a mine. 'Gugh,' gasped Briggs, floundering in his camphor.

He came to the conclusion that he was suffocating

By this time my mother, still shouting, pursued by Herman, still shouting, was trying to open the door to the attic, in order to go up and get my father's body out of the wreckage. The door was stuck, however, and wouldn't yield. Her frantic pulls on it only added to the general banging and confusion. Roy and the dog were now up, the one shouting questions, the other barking.

Father, farthest away and soundest sleeper of all, had by this time been awakened by the battering on the attic door. He decided that the house was on fire. 'I'm coming, I'm coming!' he wailed in a slow, sleepy voice – it took him many minutes to regain full consciousness. My mother, still believing he was caught under the bed, detected in his 'I'm coming!' the mournful, resigned note of one who is preparing to meet his Maker. 'He's dying!' she shouted.

'I'm all right!' Briggs yelled to reassure her. 'I'm all right!' He still believed that it was his own closeness to death that was worrying mother. I found at last the light switch in my room, unlocked the door, and Briggs and I joined the others at the attic door. The dog, who never did like Briggs, jumped for him – assuming that he was the culprit in whatever was going on – and Roy had to throw Rex and hold him. We could hear father crawling out of bed upstairs. Roy pulled the attic door open with a mighty jerk, and father came down the stairs, sleepy and irritable but safe and sound. My mother began to weep when she saw him. Rex began to howl. 'What in the name of God is going on here?' asked father.

The situation was finally put together like a gigantic jig-saw puzzle. Father caught a cold from prowling around in his bare feet but there were no other bad results. 'I'm glad,' said mother, who always looked on the bright side of things, 'that your grandfather wasn't here.'

Roy had to throw Rex

The Car We Had to Push

Many autobiographers, among them Lincoln Steffens and Gertrude Atherton, described earthquakes their families have been in. I am unable to do this because my family was never in an earthquake, but we went through a number of things in Columbus that were a great deal like earthquakes. I remember in particular some of the repercussions of an old Reo we had that wouldn't go unless you pushed it for quite a way and suddenly let your clutch out. Once, we had been able to start the engine easily by cranking it, but we had had the car for so many years that finally it wouldn't go unless you pushed it and let your clutch out. Of course, it took more than one person to do this; it took sometimes as many as five or six, depending on the grade of the roadway and conditions underfoot. The car was unusual in that the clutch and brake were on the same pedal, making it quite easy to stall the engine after it got started, so that the car would have to be pushed again.

My father used to get sick at his stomach pushing the car, and very often was unable to go to work. He had never liked the machine, even when it was good, sharing my ignorance and suspicion of all automobiles of twenty years ago and longer. The

It took sometimes as many as five or six

The Get-Ready man

boys I went to school with used to be able to identify every car as it passed by: Thomas Flyer, Firestone-Columbus, Stevens Duryea, Rambler, Winton, White Steamer, etc. I never could. The only car I was really interested in was one that the Get Ready Man, as we called him, rode around town in : a big Red Devil with a door in the back. The Get-Ready Man was a lank unkempt elderly gentleman with wild eyes and a deep voice who used to go about shouting at people through a megaphone to prepare for the end of the world. 'GET READY! GET READ-Y!' he would bellow. 'THE WORLLLD IS COMING TO AN FND!' His startling exhortations would come up, like summer thunder, at the most unexpected times and in the most surprising places. I remember once during Mantell's production of 'King Lear' at the Colonial Theatre, that the Get-Ready Man added his bawlings to the squealing of Edgar and the ranting of the King and the mouthing of the Fool, rising from somewhere in the balcony to join in. The theatre was in absolute darkness and there were rumblings of thunder and flashes of lightning offstage. Neither father nor I, who were there, ever completely got over the scene, which went something like this:

   Edgar: Tom's a-cold. – O, do de, do de, do de! – Bless thee from whirlwinds, star-blasting, and taking . . . the foul fiend vexes!
                                          (*Thunder off.*
   Lear: What! Have his daughters brought him to this pass? –
   Get-Ready Man: Get ready! Get ready!

Edgar: Pillicock sat on Pillicock-hill: —
                            Halloo, halloo, loo, loo!
                                (*Lightning flashes.*
Get-Ready Man: The Worllld is com-ing to an End!
Fool: This cold night will turn us all to fools and madmen!
Edgar: Take heed o' the foul fiend: obey thy paren —
Get-Ready Man: Get *Rea*-dy!
Edgar: Tom's a-*cold*!
Get-Ready Man: The *Worr*-uld is coming to an end! . . .

They found him finally, and ejected him, still shouting. The
Theatre, in our time, has known few such moments.

But to get back to the automobile. One of my happiest
memories of it was when, in its eighth year, my brother Roy got
together a great many articles from the kitchen, placed them in a
square of canvas, and swung this under the car with a string
attached to it so that, at a twitch, the canvas would give way and
the steel and tin things would clatter to the street. This was a little
scheme of Roy's to frighten father who had always expected the
car might explode. It worked perfectly. That was twenty-five years
ago, but it is one of the few things in my life I would like to live over
again if I could. I don't suppose that I can, now. Roy twitched the
string in the middle of a lovely afternoon, on Bryden Road near
Eighteenth Street. Father had closed his eyes and, with his hat off,
was enjoying a cool breeze. The clatter on the asphalt was tre-
mendously effective: knives, forks, can-openers, pie pans, pot
lids, biscuit-cutters, ladles, egg-beaters fell, beautifully together,
in a lingering, clamant crash. 'Stop the *car*!' shouted father. 'I
can't,' Roy said. 'The engine fell out.' 'God Almighty!' said father,
who knew what *that* meant, or knew what it sounded as if it might
mean.

It ended unhappily, of course, because we finally had to drive
back and pick up the stuff and even father knew the difference
between the works of an automobile and the equipment of a
pantry. My mother wouldn't have known, however, nor *her*
mother. My mother, for instance, thought — or, rather, knew — that
it was dangerous to drive an automobile without gasoline: it fried
the valves, or something. 'Now don't you dare drive all over town
without gasoline!' she would say to us when we started off.
Gasoline, oil, and water were much the same to her, a fact that
made her life both confusing and perilous. Her greatest dread,
however, was the Victrola — we had a very early one, back in the

Electricity was leaking all over the house

He caught the same disease that was killing the chestnut trees

'Come Josephine in My Flying Machine' days. She had an idea
that the Victrola might blow up. It alarmed her, rather than reas-
sured her, to explain that the phonograph was run neither by
gasoline nor by electricity. She could only suppose that it was
propelled by some newfangled and untested apparatus which was
likely to let go at any minute, making us all the victims and martyrs
of the wild-eyed Edison's dangerous experiments. The telephone
she was comparatively at peace with, except, of course, during
storms, when for some reason or other she always took the
receiver off the hook and let it hang. She came naturally by her
confused and groundless fears, for her own mother lived the latter
years of her life in the horrible suspicion that electricity was
dripping invisibly all over the house. It leaked, she contended, out
of empty sockets if the wall switch had been left on. She would go
around screwing in bulbs, and if they lighted up she would hastily
and fearfully turn off the wall switch and go back to her *Pearson's*
or *Everybody's*, happy in the satisfaction that she had stopped not
only a costly but a dangerous leakage. Nothing could ever clear
this up for her.

Our poor old Reo came to a horrible end, finally. We had
parked it too far from the kerb on a street with a car line. It was late
at night and the street was dark. The first streetcar that came along
couldn't get by. It picked up the tired old automobile as a terrier
might seize a rabbit and drubbed it unmercifully, losing its hold
now and then but catching a new grip a second later. Tyres
booped and whooshed, the fenders queeled and graked, the
steering-wheel rose up like a spectre and disappeared in the
direction of Franklin Avenue with a melancholy whistling sound,
bolts and gadgets flew like sparks from a Catherine wheel. It was a
splendid spectacle but, of course, saddening to everybody (except
the motorman of the streetcar, who was sore). I think some of us
broke down and wept. It must have been the weeping that caused
grandfather to take on so terribly. Time was all mixed up in his
mind; automobiles and the like he never remembered having
seen. He apparently gathered, from the talk and excitement and
weeping, that somebody had died. Nor did he let go of this
delusion. He insisted, in fact, after almost a week in which we
strove mightily to divert him, that it was a sin and a shame and a
disgrace on the family to put the funeral off any longer. 'Nobody is
dead! The automobile is smashed!' shouted my father, trying for
the thirtieth time to explain the situation to the old man. 'Was he
drunk?' demanded grandfather, sternly. 'Was who drunk?' asked

father. 'Zenas,' said grandfather. He had a name for the corpse now: it was his brother Zenas, who, as it happened, *was* dead, but not from driving an automobile while introxicated. Zenas had died in 1866. A sensitive, rather poetical boy of twenty-one when the Civil War broke out, Zenas had gone to South America – 'just', as he wrote back, 'until it blows over'. Returning after the war had blown over, he caught the same disease that was killing off the chestnut trees in those years, and passed away. It was the only case in history where a tree doctor had to be called in to spray a person, and our family had felt it very keenly; nobody else in the United States caught the blight. Some of us have looked upon Zenas' fate as a kind of poetic justice.

Now that grandfather knew, so to speak, who was dead, it became increasingly awkward to go on living in the same house with him as if nothing had happened. He would go into towering rages in which he threatened to write to the Board of Health unless the funeral were held at once. We realized that something had to be done. Eventually, we persuaded a friend of father's, named George Martin, to dress up in the manner and costume of the eighteen-sixties and pretend to be Uncle Zenas, in order to set grandfather's mind at rest. The impostor looked fine and impressive in sideburns and a high beaver hat, and not unlike the daguerreotypes of Zenas in our album. I shall never forget the night, just after dinner, when this Zenas walked into the living-room. Grandfather was stomping up and down, tall, hawk-nosed, round-oathed. The newcomer held out both his hands. 'Clem!' he cried to grandfather. Grandfather turned slowly, looked at the intruder, and snorted. 'Who air *you*?' he demanded in his deep, resonant voice. 'I'm Zenas!' cried Martin. 'Your brother Zenas, fit as a fiddle and sound as a dollar!' 'Zenas, my foot!' said grandfather. 'Zenas died of the chestnut blight in '66!'

Grandfather was given to these sudden, unexpected, and extremely lucid moments; they were generally more embarrassing than his other moments. He comprehended before he went to bed that night that the old automobile had been destroyed and that its destruction had caused all the turmoil in the house. 'It flew all to pieces, Pa,' my mother told him, in graphically describing the accident. 'I knew 'twould,' growled grandfather. 'I allus told ye to git a Pope-Toledo.'

The Day the Dam Broke

My memories of what my family and I went through during the 1913 flood in Ohio I would gladly forget. And yet neither the hardships we endured nor the turmoil and confusion we experienced can alter my feeling toward my native state and city. I am having a fine time now and wish Columbus were here, but if anyone ever wished a city was in hell it was during that frightful and perilous afternoon in 1913 when the dam broke, or, to be more exact, when everybody in town thought that the dam broke. We were both ennobled and demoralised by the experience. Granfather especially rose to magnificent heights which can never lose their splendour for me, even though his reactions to the flood were based upon a profound misconception; namely, that Nathan Bedford Forrest's cavalry was the menace we were called upon to face. The only possible means of escape for us was to flee the house, a step which grandfather sternly forbade, brandishing his old army sabre in his hand. 'Let the sons — —— come!' he roared. Meanwhile hundreds of people were streaming by our house in wild panic, screaming 'Go east! Go east!' We had to stun grandfather with the ironing board. Impeded as we were by the inert form of the old gentleman – he was taller than six feet and weighed almost a hundred and seventy pounds – we were passed, in the first half-mile, by practically everybody else in the city. Had grandfather not come to, at the corner of Parsons Avenue and Town Street, we would unquestionably have been overtaken and engulfed by the roaring waters – that is, if there had *been* any roaring waters. Later, when the panic had died down and people had gone rather sheepishly back to their homes and their offices, minimising the distances they had run and offering various reasons for running, city engineers pointed out that even if the dam had broken, the water level would not have risen more than two additional inches in the West Side. The West Side was, at the time of the dam scare, under thirty feet of water – as, indeed, were all Ohio river towns during the great spring floods of twenty years ago. The East Side (where we lived and where all the running occurred) had never been in any danger at all. Only a rise of some ninety-five feet could have caused the flood waters to flow over

High Street – the thoroughfare that divided the east side of town
from the west – and engulf the East Side.

The fact that we were all as safe as kittens under a cookstove did
not, however, assuage in the least the fine despair and the grotes-
que desperation which seized upon the residents of the East Side
when the cry spread like a grass fire that the dam had given way.
Some of the most dignified, staid, cynical, and clear-thinking men
in town abandoned their wives, stenographers, homes, and offices
and ran east. There are few alarms in the world more terrifying
than 'The dam has broken!' There are few persons capable of
stopping to reason when that clarion cry strikes upon their ears,
even persons who live in towns no nearer than five hundred miles
to a dam.

The Columbus, Ohio, broken-dam rumour began, as I recall it,
about noon of 12 March 1913. High Street, the main canyon of
trade, was loud with the placid hum of business and the buzzing of
placid businessmen arguing, computing, wheedling, offering,
refusing, compromising. Dari Conningway, one of the foremost
corporation lawyers in the Middle-West, was telling the Public
Utilities Commission in the language of Julius Caesar that they
might as well try to move the Northern star as to move him. Other
men were making their little boasts and their little gestures. Suddenly somebody began to run. It may be that he had simply
remembered, all of a moment, an engagement to meet his wife, for
which he was now frightfully late. Whatever it was, he ran east on
Broad Street (probably toward the Maramor Restaurant, a favourite place for a man to meet his wife). Somebody else began to run,
perhaps a newsboy in high spirits. Another man, a portly gentleman of affairs, broke into a trot. Inside of ten minutes, everybody
on High Street, from the Union Depot to the Courthouse was
running. A loud mumble gradually crystalized into the dread word
'dam.' 'The dam has broke!' The fear was put into words by a little
old lady in an electric, or by a traffic cop, or by a small boy:
nobody knows who, nor does it now really matter. Two thousand
people were abruptly in full flight. 'Go east!,' was the cry that
arose – east away from the river, east to safety. 'Go east! Go east!
Go east!'

Black streams of people flowed eastward down all the streets
leading in that direction; these streams, whose headwaters were
in the drygoods stores, office buildings, harness shops, movie
theatres, were fed by trickles of housewives, children, cripples,
servants, dogs, and cats, slipping out of the houses past which the

Two thousand people were in full flight

main streams flowed, shouting and screaming. People ran out
leaving fires burning and food cooking and doors wide open. I
remember, however, that my mother turned out all the fires and
that she took with her a dozen eggs and two loaves of bread. It was
her plan to make Memorial Hall, just two blocks away, and take
refuge somewhere in the top of it, in one of the dusty rooms where
war veterans met and where old battle flags and stage scenery
were stored. But the seething throngs, shouting 'Go east!' drew her
along and the rest of us with her. When grandfather regained full
consciousness, at Parsons Avenue, he turned upon the retreating
mob like a vengeful prophet and exhorted the men to form ranks
and stand off the Rebel dogs, but at length he, too, got the idea that
the dam had broken and, roaring 'Go east!' in his powerful voice,
he caught up in one arm a small child and in the other a slight
clerkish man of perhaps forty-two and we slowly began to gain on
those ahead of us.

A scattering of firemen, policemen, and army officers in dress uniforms – there had been a review at Fort Hayes, in the northern part of town – added colour to the surging billows of people. 'Go east!' cried a little child in a piping voice, as she ran past a porch on which drowsed a lieutenant-colonel of infantry. Used to quick decisions, trained to immediate obedience, the officer bounded off the porch and, running at full tilt, soon passed the child, bawling 'Go east!' The two of them emptied rapidly the houses of the little street they were on. 'What is it? What is it?' demanded a fat, waddling man who intercepted the colonel. The officer dropped behind and asked the little child what it was. 'The dam has broke!' gasped the girl. 'The dam has broke!' roared the colonel. 'Go east! Go east! Go east!' He was soon leading, with the exhausted child in his arms, a fleeing company of three hundred persons who had gathered around him from living-rooms, shops, garages, backyards, and basements.

Nobody has ever been able to compute with any exactness how many people took part in the great rout of 1913, for the panic, which extended from the Winslow Bottling Works in the south end to Clintonville, six miles north, ended as abruptly as it began and the bobtail and ragtag and velvet-gowned groups of refugees melted away and slunk home, leaving the streets peaceful and deserted. The shouting, weeping, tangled evacuation of the city lasted not more than two hours in all. Some few people got as far east as Reynoldsburg, twelve miles away; fifty or more reached the Country Club, eight miles away; most of the others gave up, exhausted, or climbed trees in Franklin Park, four miles out. Order was restored and fear dispelled finally by means of militiamen riding about in motor lorries bawling through megaphones: 'The dam has *not* broken!' At first this tended only to add to the confusion and increase the panic, for many stampeders thought the soldiers were bellowing 'The dam has now broken!,' thus setting an official seal of authentication on the calamity.

All the time, the sun shone quietly and there was nowhere any sign of oncoming waters. A visitor in an airplane, looking down on the straggling, agitated masses of people below, would have been hard put to it to divine a reason for the phenomenon. It must have inspired, in such an observer, a peculiar kind of terror, like the sight of the *Marie Celeste*, abandoned at sea, its galley fires peacefully burning, its tranquil decks bright in the sunlight.

An aunt of mine, Aunt Edith Taylor, was in a movie theatre on High Street when, over and above the sound of the piano in the pit (a W. S. Hart picture was being shown), there rose the steadily increasing tromp of running feet. Persistent shouts rose above the tromping. An elderly man, sitting near my aunt, mumbled something, got out of his seat, and went up the aisle at a dogtrot. This started everybody. In an instant the audience was jamming the aisles. 'Fire!' shouted a woman who always expected to be burned up in a theatre; but now the shouts outside were louder and coherent. 'The dam has broke!' cried somebody. 'Go east!' screamed a small woman in front of my aunt. And east they went, pushing and shoving and clawing, knocking women and children down, emerging finally into the street, torn and sprawling. Inside the theatre, Bill Hart was calmly calling some desperado's bluff and the brave girl at the piano played 'Row! Row! Row!' loudly and then 'In My Harem.' Outside, men were streaming across the Statehouse yard, others were climbing trees, a woman managed to get up onto the 'These Are My Jewels' statue, whose bronze figures of Sherman, Stanton, Grant, and Sheridan watched with cold unconcern the going to pieces of the capital city.

'I ran south to State Street, east on State to Third, south on Third to Town, and out east on Town,' my Aunt Edith has written me. 'A tall spare woman with grim eyes and a determined chin ran past me down the middle of the street. I was still uncertain as to what was the matter, in spite of all the shouting. I drew up alongside the woman with some effort, for although she was in her late fifties, she had a beautiful easy running form and seemed to be in excellent condition. "What is it?" I puffed. She gave me a quick glance and then looked ahead again, stepping up her pace a trifle. "Don't ask me, ask God!" she said.

'When I reached Grant Avenue, I was so spent that Dr H. R. Mallory – you remember Dr Mallory, the man with the white beard who looks like Robert Browning? – well, Dr Mallory whom I had drawn away from at the corner of Fifth and Town, passed me. "It's got us!" he shouted, and I felt sure that whatever it was *did* have us, for you know what conviction Dr Mallory's statements always carried. I didn't know at the time what he meant, but I found out later. There was a boy behind him on roller-skates, and Dr Mallory mistook the swishing of the skates for the sound of rushing water. He eventually reached the Columbus School for Girls, at the corner of Parsons Avenue and Town Street, where he collapsed, expecting the cold frothing waters of the Scioto to sweep him into oblivion. The boy on the skates swirled past him and Dr Mallory realized for the first time what he had been

'It's got us!' He shouted

running from. Looking back up the street, he could see no signs of water, but nevertheless, after resting a few minutes, he jogged on east again. He caught up with me at Ohio Avenue, where we rested together. I should say that about seven hundred people passed us. A funny thing was that all of them were on foot. Nobody seemed to have had the courage to stop and start his car; but as I remember it, all cars had to be cranked in those days, which is probably the reason.'

The next day, the city went about its business as if nothing had happened, but there was no joking. It was two years or more before you dared treat the breaking of the dam lightly. And even now, twenty years after, there are a few persons, like Dr Mallory, who will shut up like a clam if you mention the Afternoon of the great Run.

The Night the Ghost Got In

The ghost that got into our house on the night of 17 November 1915, raised such a hullabaloo of misunderstandins that I am sorry I didn't just let it keep on walking, and go to bed. Its advent caused my mother to throw a shoe through a window of the house next door and ended up with my grandfather shooting a patrolman. I am sorry, therefore, as I have said, that I ever paid any attention to the footsteps.

They began about a quarter past one o'clock in the morning, a rhythmic, quick-cadenced walking around the dining-room table. My mother was asleep in one room upstairs, my brother Herman in another; grandfather was in the attic, in the old walnut bed which, as you will remember, once fell on my father. I had just stepped out of the bathtub and was busily rubbing myself with a towel when I heard the steps. They were the steps of a man walking rapidly around the dining-room table downstairs. The light from the bathroom shone down the back steps, which dropped directly into the dining-room; I could see the faint shine of plates on the plate-rail; I couldn't see the table. The steps kept going round and round the table; at regular intervals a board creaked, when it was trod upon. I supposed at first that it was my father or my brother Roy, who had gone to Indianapolis but were expected home at any time. I suspected next that it was a burglar. It did not enter my mind until later that it was a ghost.

After the walking had gone on for perhaps three minutes, I tiptoed to Herman's room. 'Psst!' I hissed, in the dark, shaking him. 'Awp,' he said, in the low, hopeless tone of a despondent beagle – he always half suspected that something would 'get him' in the night. I told him who I was. 'There's something downstairs!' I said. He got up and followed me to the head of the back staircase. We listened together. There was no sound. The steps had ceased. Herman looked at me in some alarm: I had only the bath towel around my waist. He wanted to go back to bed, but I gripped his arm. 'There's something down there!' I said. Instantly the steps began again, circled the dining-room table like a man running, and started up the stairs toward us, heavily, two at a time. The light still shone palely down the stairs; we saw nothing coming; we

He always half suspected that something would get him

only heard the steps. Herman rushed to his room and slammed the door. I slammed shut the door at the stairs top and held my knee against it. After a long minute, I slowly opened it again. There was nothing there. There was no sound. None of us ever heard the ghost again.

The slamming of the doors had aroused mother: she peered out of her room. 'What on earth are you boys doing?' she demanded. Herman ventured out of his room. 'Nothing,' he said, gruffly, but he was, in colour, a light green. 'What was all that running downstairs?' said mother. So she had heard the steps, too! We just looked at her. 'Burglars!' she shouted intuitively. I tried to quiet her by starting lightly downstairs.

'Come on, Herman,' I said.

'I'll stay with mother,' he said. 'She's all excited.'

I stepped back onto the landing.

'Don't either of you go a step,' said mother. 'We'll call the police.' Since the phone was downstairs, I didn't see how we were going to call the police – nor did I want the police – but mother made one of her quick, incomparable decisions. She flung up a window of her bedroom which faced the bedroom windows of the house of a neighbour, picked up a shoe, and whammed it through a pane of glass across the narrow space that separated the two houses. Glass tinkled into the bedroom occupied by a retired engraver named Bodwell and his wife. Bodwell had been for some years in rather a bad way and was subject to mild 'attacks'. Most everybody we knew or lived near had *some* kind of attacks.

It was now about two o'clock of a moonless night; clouds hung black and low. Bodwell was at the window in a minute, shouting, frothing a little, shaking his fist. 'We'll sell the house and go back to Peoria,' we could hear Mrs Bodwell. 'Burglars!' she shouted. 'Burglars in the house!' Herman and I hadn't dared to tell her that it was not burglars but ghosts, for she was even more afraid of ghosts than of burglars. Bodwell at first thought that she meant there were burglars in his house, but finally he quieted down and called the police for us over an extension phone by his bed. After he had disappeared from the window, mother suddenly made as if to throw another shoe, not because there was further need of it but, as she later explained, because the thrill of heaving a shoe through a window glass had enormously taken her fancy. I prevented her.

The police were on hand in a commendably short time: a Ford sedan full of them, two on motorcycles, and a patrol wagon with about eight in it and a few reporters. They began banging at our front door. Flashlights shot streaks of gleam up and down the walls, across the yard, down the walk between our house and Bodwell's. 'Open up!' cried a hoarse voice. 'We're men from Headquarters!' I wanted to go down and let them in, since there they were, but mother wouldn't hear of it. 'You haven't a stitch on,' she pointed out. 'You'd catch your death.' I wound the towel around me again. Finally the cops put their shoulders to our big heavy front door with its thick beveled glass and broke it in: I could hear a rending of wood and a splash of glass on the floor of the hall. Their lights played all over the living-room and criss-crossed nervously in the dining-room, stabbed into hallways, shot up the front stairs and finally up the back. They caught me standing in my towel at the top. A heavy policeman bounded up the steps. 'Who are you?' he demanded. 'I live here,' I said. 'Well, whattsa matta, ya hot?' he asked. It was, as a matter of fact, cold; I went to my room and pulled on some trousers. On my way out, a cop stuck a gun into my ribs. 'Whatta you doin' here?' he demanded. 'I live here,' I said

The officer in charge reported to mother. 'No sign of nobody, lady,' he said. 'Musta got away — whatt'd he look like?' 'There were two or three of them,' mother said, 'whooping and carrying on and slamming doors.' 'Funny,' said the cop. 'All ya windows and doors was locked on the inside tight as a tick.'

Downstairs, we could hear the tromping of other police. Police were all over the place; doors were yanked open, drawers were yanked open, windows were shot up and pulled down, furniture fell with dull thumps. A half-dozen policemen emerged out of the darkness of the front hallway upstairs. They began to ransack the floor: pulled beds away from walls, tore clothes off hooks in the closets, pulled suitcases and boxes of shelves. One of them found an old zither that Roy had won in a pool tournament. 'Looky here, Joe,' he said strumming it with a big paw. The cop named Joe took it and turned it over. 'What is it?' he asked me. 'It's an old zither our guinea pig used to sleep on,' I said. It was true that a pet guinea we once had would never sleep anywhere except on the zither, but I should never have said so. Joe and the other cop looked at me a long time. They put the zither back on a shelf.

Police were all over the place

'No sign o' nuthin',' said the cop who had first spoken to mother. 'This guy,' he explained to the others, jerking a thumb at me, 'was nekked. The lady seems historical.' They all nodded, but said nothing; just looked at me. In the small silence we all heard a creaking in the attic. Grandfather was turning over in bed. 'What's 'at?' snapped Joe. Five or six cops sprang for the attic door before I could intervene or explain. I realised that it would be bad if they burst in on grandfather unannounced, or even announced. He was going through a phase in which he believed that General Meade's men, under steady hammering by Stonewall Jackson, were beginning to retreat and even desert.

When I got to the attic, things were pretty confused. Grandfather had evidently jumped to the conclusion that the police were deserters from Meade's army, trying to hide away in his attic. He bounded out of bed wearing a long flannel nightgown over long woollen underwear, a nightcap, and a leather jacket around his chest. The cops must have realised at once that the indignant white-haired old man belonged in the house, but they had no chance to say so. 'Back, ye cowardly dogs!' roared grandfather. 'Back t' the lines, ye goddam lily-livered cattle!' With that, he fetched the officer who found the zither a flat-handed smack alongside his head that sent him sprawling. The others beat a retreat, but not fast enough; grandfather grabbed Zither's gun from its holster and let fly. The report seemed to crack the rafters; smoke filled the attic. A cop cursed and shot his hand to his shoulder. Somehow, we all finally got downstairs again and locked the door against the old gentleman. He fired once or twice more in the darkness and then went back to bed. 'That was grandfather,' I explained to Joe, out of breath. 'He thinks you're deserters.' 'I'll say he does,' said Joe.

The cops were reluctant to leave without getting their hands on somebody besides grandfather; the night had been distinctly a defeat for them. Furthermore, they obviously didn't like the 'layout;' something looked – and I can see their viewpoint – phony. They began to poke into things again. A reporter, a thin-faced, wispy man, came up to me. I had put on one of mother's blouses, not being able to find anything else. The reporter looked at me with mingled suspicion and interest. 'Just what the hell is the real lowdown here, Bud?' he asked. I decided to be frank with him. 'We had ghosts,' I said. He gazed at me a long time as if I were a slot machine into which he had, without results, dropped a nickel. Then he walked away. The cops followed him, the one grand-

father shot holding his now-bandaged arm, cursing and blas-
pheming. 'I'm gonna get my gun back from that old bird,' said the
zither-cop. 'Yeh,' said Joe. 'You – and who else?' I told them I
would bring it to the station house the next day.

'What was the matter with that one policeman?' mother asked,
after they had gone. 'Grandfather shot him,' I said. 'What for?' she
demanded. I told her he was a deserter. 'Of all things!' said
mother. 'He was such a nice-looking young man.'

Grandfather was fresh as a daisy and full of jokes at breakfast
next morning. We thought at first he had forgotten all about what
had happened, but he hadn't. Over his third cup of coffee, he
glared at Herman and me. 'What was the idee of all them cops
tarryhootin' round the house last night?' he demanded. He had us
there.

More Alarms at Night

One of the incidents that I always think of first when I cast back over my youth is what happened the night that my father 'threatened to get Buck.' This, as you will see, is not precisely a fair or accurate description of what actually occurred, but it is the way in which I and the other members of my family invariably allude to the occasion. We were living at the time in an old house at 77 Lexington Avenue, in Columbus, Ohio. In the early years of the nineteenth century, Columbus won out, as state capital, by only one vote over Lancaster, and ever since then has had the hallucination that it is being followed, a curious municipal state of mind which affects, in some way or other, all those who live there. Columbus is a town in which almost anything is likely to happen and in which almost everything has.

My father was sleeping in the front room on the second floor next to that of my brother Roy, who was then about sixteen. Father was usually in bed by nine-thirty and up again by ten-thirty to protest bitterly against a Victrola record we three boys were in the habit of playing over and over, namely, 'No News, or What Killed the Dog,' a recitation by Nat Wills. The record had been played so many times that its grooves were deeply cut and the needle often kept revolving in the same groove, repeating over and over the same words. Thus: 'ate some burnt hoss flesh, ate some burnt hoss flesh, ate some burnt hoss flesh.' It was this reiteration that generally got father out of bed.

On the night in question, however, we had all gone to bed at about the same time, without much fuss. Roy, as a matter of fact, had been in bed all day with a kind of mild fever. It wasn't severe enough to cause delirium and my brother was the last person in the world to give way to delirium. Nevertheless, he had warned father when father went to bed, that he *might* become delirious.

About three o'clock in the morning, Roy, who was wakeful, decided to pretend that delirium was on him, in order to have, as he later explained it, some 'fun'. He got out of bed and, going to my father's room, shook him and said, 'Buck, your time has come!' My father's name was not Buck but Charles, nor had he ever been called Buck. He was a tall, mildly nervous peaceable gentleman, given to quiet pleasures, and eager that everything should run smoothly. 'Hmm?' he said, with drowsy bewilderment. 'Get up, Buck,' said my brother, coldly, but with a certain gleam in his eyes. My father leaped out of bed, on the side away from his son, rushed from the room, locked the door behind him, and shouted us all up.

We were naturally reluctant to believe that Roy, who was quiet and self-contained, had threatened his father with any such abracadabra as father said he had. My older brother, Herman, went back to bed without any comment. 'You've had a bad dream,' my mother said. This vexed my father. 'I tell you he called me Buck and told me my time had come,' he said. We went to the door of his room, unlocked it, and tiptoed through it to Roy's room. He lay in his bed, breathing easily, as if he were fast asleep. It was apparent at a glance that he did not have a high fever. My mother gave my father a look. 'I tell you he did,' whispered father.

Our presence in the room finally seemed to awaken Roy and he was (or rather, as we found out long afterward, pretended to be) astonished and bewildered. 'What's the matter?' he asked. 'Nothing,' said my mother. 'Just your father had a nightmare.' 'I did not have a nightmare,' said father, slowly and firmly. He wore an old-fashioned, 'side-slit' nightgown which looked rather odd on his tall, spare figure. The situation, before we let it drop and everybody went back to bed again, became, as such situations in our family usually did, rather more complicated than ironed out. Roy demanded to know what had happened, and my mother told him, in considerably garbled fashion, what father had told her. At this a light dawned in Roy's eyes. 'Dad's got it backward,' he said. He then explained that he had heard father get out of bed and had called to him. 'I'll handle this,' his father had answered. 'Buck is downstairs.' 'Who is this Buck?' my mother demanded of father. 'I don't know any Buck and I never said that,' father contended, irritably. None of us (except Roy, of course) believed him. 'You had a dream,' said mother. 'People have these dreams.' 'I did not have a dream,' father said. He was pretty well nettled by this time, and he stood in front of a bureau mirror, brushing his hair with a pair of military brushes; it always seemed to calm father to brush his hair. My mother declared that it was 'a sin and a shame' for a grown man to wake up a sick boy simply because he (the grown man: father) had got on his back and had a bad dream. My father, as a matter of fact, *had* been known to have nightmares, usually about Lillian Russell and President Cleveland, who chased him.

We argued the thing for perhaps another half-hour, after which mother made father sleep in her room. 'You're all safe now, boys,' she said, firmly, as she shut her door I could hear father grumbling for a long time, with an occasional monosyllable of doubt from mother.

It was some six months after this that father went through a similar experience with me. He was at that time sleeping in the room next to mine. I had been trying all afternoon, in vain, to think of the name Perth Amboy. It seems now like a very simple name to recall and yet on the day in question I thought of every other town in the country, as well as such words and names and phrases as terra cotta, Walla-Walla, bill of lading, vice versa, hoity-toity, Pall Mall, Bodley Head, Schumann-Heink, etc., without even coming close to Perth Amboy. I suppose terra cotta was the closest I came, although it was not very close.

Long after I had gone to bed, I was struggling with the problem. I began to indulge in the wildest fancies as I lay there in the dark, such as that there was no such town, and even that there was no such state as New Jersey. I fell to repeating the word 'Jersey' over and over again, until it became idiotic and meaningless. If you have ever lain awake at night and repeated one word over and over, thousands and millions and hundreds of thousands of millions of times, you know the disturbing mental state you can get into. I got to thinking that there was nobody else in the world but me, and various other wild imaginings of that nature. Eventually, lying there thinking these outlandish thoughts, I grew slightly alarmed. I began to suspect that one might lose one's mind over some such trivial mental tic as a futile search for terra firma Piggly Wiggly Gorgonzola Prester John Arc de Triomphe Holy Moses Lares and Penates. I began to feel the imperative necessity of human contact. This silly and alarming tangle of thought and fancy had gone far enough. I might get into some kind of mental aberrancy unless I found out the name of that Jersey town and could go to sleep. Therefore, I got out of bed, walked into the room where father was sleeping, and shook him. 'Um!' he mumbled. I shook him more fiercely and he finally woke up, with a glaze of dream and apprehension in his eyes. 'What's matter?' he asked, thickly. I must, indeed, have been rather wild of eye, and my hair, which is unruly, becomes monstrously tousled and snarled at night. 'Wha's it?' said my father, sitting up, in readiness to spring out of bed on the far side. The thought must have been going through his mind that all his sons were crazy, or on the verge of going crazy. I see that now, but I didn't then, for I had forgotten the Buck incident and did not realise how similar my appearance must have been to Roy's the night he called father Buck and told him his time had come. 'Listen,' I said. 'Name some towns in New Jersey quick!' It must have been around three in the morning. Father got up, keeping the bed between him and me, and started to pull his trousers on. 'Don't bother about dressing,' I said. 'Just name some towns in New Jersey.' While he hastily pulled on his clothes – I remember he left his socks off and put his shoes on his bare feet – father began to name, in a shaky voice various New Jersey cities. I can still see him reaching for his coat without taking his eyes off me. 'Newark,' he said, 'Jersey City, Atlantic City, Elizabeth, Paterson, Passaic, Trenton, Jersey City, Trenton, Paterson –' 'It has two names,' I snapped. 'Elizabeth and Paterson,' he said. 'No, no!' I told him, irritably. 'This is one town with one name, but there are two words in it, like helter-skelter.' 'Helter-skelter,' said my father, moving slowly toward the bedroom door and smiling in a faint, strained way which I understand now – but didn't then – was meant to humour me. When he was within a few paces of the door, he fairly leaped for it and ran out into the hall, his coat-tails and shoelaces flying. The exit stunned me. I had no notion that he thought I had gone out of my senses; I could only believe that he had gone out of *his* or that, only partially awake, he was engaged in some form of running in his sleep. I ran after him and I caught him at the door of mother's room and grabbed him, in order to reason with him. I shook him a little, thinking to wake him completely. 'Mary! Roy! Herman!' he shouted. I, too, began to shout for my brothers and my mother. My mother opened her door instantly, and there we were at 3:30 in the morning grappling and shouting, father partly dressed, but without socks or shirt, and I in pyjamas.

'Now, what?' demanded my mother, grimly, pulling us apart. She was capable, fortunately, of handling any two of us and she never in her life was alarmed by the words or actions of any one of us.

'Look out for Jamie!' said father. (He always called me Jamie when excited.) My mother looked at me.

'What's the matter with your father?' she demanded. I said I didn't know; I said he had got up suddenly and dressed and ran out of the room.

'Where did you think you were going?' mother asked him,

coolly. He looked at me. We looked at each other, breathing hard, but somewhat calmer.

'He was babbling about New Jersey at this infernal hour of the night,' said father. 'He came to my room and asked me to name towns in New Jersey.' Mother looked at me.

'I just asked him,' I said. 'I was trying to think of one and couldn't sleep.'

'You see?' said father, triumphantly. Mother didn't look at him.

'Get to bed, both of you,' she said. 'I don't want to hear any more out of you tonight. Dressing and tearing up and down the hall at this hour in the morning!' She went back into the room and shut her door. Father and I went back to bed. 'Are you all right?' he called to me. 'Are you?' I asked. 'Well, good night,' he said. 'Good night,' I said.

Mother would not let the rest of us discuss the affair next morning at breakfast. Herman asked what the hell had been the matter. 'We'll go on to something more elevating,' said mother.

A Sequence of Servants

When I look back on the long line of servants my mother hired during the years I lived at home, I remember clearly ten or twelve of them (we had about a hundred and sixty-two, all told, but few of them were memorable). There was, among the immortals, Dora Gedd, a quiet, mousy girl of thirty-two who one night shot at a man in her room, throwing our household into an uproar that was equalled perhaps only by the goings-on the night the ghost got in. Nobody knew how her lover, a morose garage man, got into the house, but everybody for two blocks knew how he got out. Dora had dressed up in a lavender evening gown for the occasion and she wore a mass of jewellery, some of which was my mother's. She kept shouting something from Shakespeare after the shooting – I forget just what – and pursued the gentleman dowstairs from her attic room. When he got to the second floor he rushed into my father's room. It was this entrance, and not the shot or the shouting, that aroused father, a deep sleeper always. 'Get me out of here!' shouted the victim. This situation rapidly developed, from then on, into one of those bewildering involvements for which my family had, I am afraid, a kind of unhappy genius. When the cops arrived Dora was shooting out the Welsbach gas mantles in the living-room, and her gentleman friend had fled. By dawn everything was quiet once more.

There were others. Gertie Straub: big, genial, and ruddy, a collector of pints of rye (we learned after she was gone), who came in after two o'clock one night from a dancing party at Buckeye Lake and awakened us by bumping into and knocking over furniture. 'Who's down there?' called mother from upstairs. 'It's me, dearie,' said Gertie, 'Gertie Straub.' 'What are you *doing*?' demanded mother. 'Dusting,' said Gertie.

Juanemma Kramer was one of my favourites. Her mother loved the name Juanita so dearly that she had worked the first part of it into the names of all her daughters – they were (in addition to a Juanita) Juanemma, Juanhelen, and Juangrace. Juanemma was a thin, nervous maid who lived in constant dread of being hypnotised. Nor were her fears unfounded, for she was so extremely susceptible to hypnotic suggestion that one evening at B. F. Keith's

'Dusting,' said Gertie

theatre when a man on the stage was hypnotised, Juanemma, in the audience, was hypnotised too and floundered out into the aisle making the same cheeping sound that the subject on the stage, who had been told he was a chicken, was making. The act was abandoned and some xylophone players were brought on to restore order. One night, when our house was deep in quiet slumber, Juanemma became hypnotised in her sleep. She dreamed that a man 'put her under' and then disappeared without 'bringing her out.' This was explained when, at last, a police surgeon whom we called in – he was the only doctor we could persuade to come out at three in the morning – slapped her into consciousness. It got so finally that any buzzing or whirling sound or any flashing object would put Juanemma under, and we had to let her go. I was reminded of her recently when, at a performance of the movie 'Rasputin and the Empress', there came the scene in which Lionel Barrymore as the unholy priest hypnotises the Czarevitch by spinning before his eyes a glittering watch. If Juanemma sat in any theatre and witnessed that scene she must, I am sure, have gone under instantly. Happily, she seems to have missed the picture, for otherwise Mr Barrymore might have had to dress up again as Rasputin (which God forbid) and journey across the country to get her out of it – excellent publicity but a great bother.

Before I go on to Vashti, whose last name I forget, I will look in passing at another of our white maids (Vashti was coloured). Belle Giddin distinguished herself by one gesture which fortunately did not result in the bedlam occasioned by Juanemma's hypnotic states or Dora Gedd's shooting spree. Bella burned her finger grievously, and purposely, one afternoon in the steam of a boiling kettle so that she could find out whether the pain-killer she had bought one night at a tent-show for fifty cents was any good. It was only fair.

Vashti turned out, in the end, to be partly legendary. She was a comely and sombre negress who was always able to find things my mother lost. 'I don't know what's become of my garnet brooch,' my mother said one day. 'Yassum,' said Vashti. In half an hour she had found it. 'Where in the world was it?' asked mother. 'In de yahd,' said Vashti. 'De dog mussa drug it out.'

Vashti was in love with a young coloured chauffeur named Charley, but she was also desired by her stepfather, whom none of us had ever seen but who was, she said, a handsome but messin' round gentleman from Georgia who had come north and married

Vashti's mother just so he could be near Vashti. Charley, her fiancé, was for killing the stepfather but we counselled flight to another city. Vashti, however, would burst into tears and hymns and vow she'd never leave us; she got a certain pleasure out of bearing her cross. Thus we all lived in jeopardy, for the possibility that Vashti, Charley, and her stepfather might fight it out some night in our kitchen did not, at times, seem remote. Once I went into the kitchen at midnight to make some coffee. Charley was standing at a window looking out into the backyard; Vashti was rolling her eyes. 'Heah he come! Heah he come!' she moaned. The stepfather didn't show up, however.

Charley finally saved up twenty-seven dollars toward taking Vashti away but one day he impulsively bought a ·22 revolver with a mother-of-pearl handle and demanded that Vashti tell him where her mother and stepfather lived. 'Doan go up dere, doan go *up* dere!' said Vashti. 'Mah mothah is just as rarin' as he is!' Charley, however, insisted. It came out then that Vashti didn't have any stepfather; there was no such person. Charley threw her over for a yellow gal named Nancy: he never forgave Vashti for the vanishing from his life of a menace that had come to mean more to him than Vashti herself. Afterwards, if you asked Vashti about her stepfather or about Charley she would say, proudly, and with a woman-of-the-world air, 'Neither one ob 'em is messin' round *me* any mo',.'

Mrs Doody, a huge, middle-aged woman with a religious taint, came into and went out of our house like a comet. The second night she was there she went berserk while doing the dishes and, under the impression that father was the Antichrist, pursued him several times up the backstairs and down the front. He had been sitting quietly over his coffee in the living-room when she burst in from the kitchen waving a bread knife. My brother Herman finally felled her with a piece of Libby's cut-glass that had been a wedding present of mother's. Mother, I remember, was in the attic at the time, trying to find some old things, and, appearing on the scene in the midst of it all, got the quick and mistaken impression that father was chasing Mrs Doody.

Mrs Robertson, a fat and mumbly old coloured woman, who might have been sixty and who might have been a hundred, gave us more than one turn during the many years that she did our washing. She had been a slave down South and she remembered 'having seen the troops marching – a mess o' blue, den a mes o' grow.' 'What,' my mother asked her once, 'were they fighting

Went berserk while doing the dishes . . .

about?' 'Dat,' said Mrs Robertson, 'Ah don't know.' She had a
feeling, at all times, that something was going to happen. I can see
her now, staggering up from the basement with a basketful of
clothes and coming abruptly to a halt in the middle of the kitchen.
'Hahk!' she would say, in a deep, guttural voice. We would all
hark; there was never anything to be heard. Neither, when she
shouted 'Look yondah!' and pointed a trembling hand at a window, was there ever anything to be seen. Father protested time
and again that he couldn't stand Mrs Robertson around, but
mother always refused to let her go. It seems that she was a jewel.
Once she walked unbidden, a dishpan full of wrung-out clothes
under her arm, into father's study, where he was engrossed in
some figures. Father looked up. She regarded him for a moment in
silence. Then – 'Look out!' she said, and withdrew. Another time,
a murky winter afternoon, she came flubbering up the cellar stairs
and bounced, out of breath, into the kitchen. Father was in the
kitchen sipping some black coffee; he was in a jittery state of
nerves from the effects of having had a tooth out, and had been in
bed most of the day. 'Dey is a death watch down-staihs!' rumbled
the old coloured lady. It developed that she had heard a strange
'chipping" noise back of the furnace. 'That was a cricket,' said
father. 'Um-*hm*,' said Mrs Robertson. 'Dat was uh death watch!'
With that she put on her hat and went home, poising just long
enough at the back door to observe darkly to father. '*Dey ain't no
way!*' It upset him for days.

Mrs Robertson had only one great hour that I can think of – Jack
Johnson's victory over Mistah Jeffries on the Fourth of July, 1910.
She took a prominent part in the coloured parade through the
South End that night, playing a Spanish fandango on a banjo. The
procession was led by the pastor of her church who, Mrs Robertson later told us, had 'splained that the victory of Jack over Mistah
Jeffries proved 'de 'speriority ob de race.' 'What,' asked my
mother, 'did he mean by that?' 'Dat', said Mrs Robertson, 'Ah
don't know.'

Our other servants I don't remember so clearly, except the one
who set the house on fire (her name eludes me), and Edda Millmoss. Edda was always slightly morose but she had gone along for
months, all the time she was with us, quietly and efficiently
attending to her work, until the night we had Carson Blair and F. R.
Gardiner to dinner – both men of importance to my father's
ambitions. Then suddenly, while serving the entrée, Edda dropped everything and, pointing a quivering finger at father, accused

him in a long rigamarole of having done her out of her rights to the land on which Trinity Church in New York stands. Mr Gardiner had one of his 'attacks' and the whole evening turned out miserably.

The Dog That Bit People

Probably no one man should have as many dogs in his life as I have had, but there was more pleasure than distress in them for me except in the case of an Airedale named Muggs. He gave me more trouble than all the other fifty-four or -five put together, although my moment of keenest embarrassment was the time a Scotch terrier named Jeannie, who had just had six puppies in the clothes closet of a fourth floor apartment in New York, had the unexpected seventh and last at the corner of Eleventh Street and Fifth Avenue during a walk she had insisted on taking. Then, too, there was the prize winning French poodle, a great big black poodle – none of your little, untroublesome white miniatures – who got sick riding in the rumble seat of a car with me on her way to the Greenwich Dog Show. She had a red rubber bib tucked around her throat and, since a rain storm came up when we were half way through the Bronx, I had to hold over her a small green umbrella, really more of a parasol. The rain beat down fearfully and suddenly the driver of the car drove into a big garage, filled with mechanics. It happened so quickly that I forgot to put the umbrella down and I will always remember, with sickening distress, the look of incredulity mixed with hatred that came over the face of the particular hardened garage man that came over to see what we wanted, when he took a look at me and the poodle. All garage men, and people of that intolerant stripe, hate poodles with their curious haircut, especially the pom-poms that you got to leave on their hips if you expect the dogs to win a prize.

But the Airedale, as I have said, was the worst of all my dogs. He really wasn't my dog, as a matter of fact: I came home from a vacation one summer to find that my brother Roy had bought him while I was away. A big, burly, choleric dog, he always acted as if he thought I wasn't one of the family. There was a slight advantage in being one of the family, for he didn't bite the family as often as he bit strangers. Still, in the years that we had him he bit everybody but mother, and he made a pass at her once but missed. That was during the month when we suddenly had mice, and Muggs refused to do anything about them. Nobody ever had mice exactly like the mice we had that month. They acted like pet mice, almost like mice somebody had trained. They were so friendly that one night when mother entertained at dinner the Friraliras, a club she and my father had belonged to for twenty years, she put down a lot of little dishes with food in them on the pantry floor so that the mice would be satisfied with that and wouldn't come into the dining room. Muggs stayed out in the pantry with the mice, lying on the floor, growling to himself – not at the mice, but about all the people in the next room that he would have liked to get at. Mother slipped out into the pantry once to see how everything was going. Everything was going fine. It made her so mad to see Muggs lying there, oblivious of the mice – they came running up to her – that she slapped him and he slashed at her, but didn't make it. He was sorry immediately, mother said. He was always sorry, she said, after he bit someone, but we could not understand how she figured this out. He didn't act sorry.

Mother used to send a box of candy every Christmas to the people the Airedale bit. The list finally contained forty or more names. Nobody could understand why we didn't get rid of the dog. I didn't understand it very well myself, but we didn't get rid of him. I think that one or two people tried to poison Muggs – he acted poisoned once in a while – and old Major Moberly fired at him once with his service revolver near the Seneca Hotel in East Broad Street – but Muggs lived to be almost eleven years old and even when he could hardly get around he bit a Congressman who had called to see my father on business. My mother had never liked the Congressman – she said the signs of his horoscope showed he couldn't be trusted (he was Saturn with the moon in Virgo) – but she sent him a box of candy that Christmas. He sent it right back, probably because he suspected it was trick candy. Mother persuaded herself it was all for the best that the dog had bitten him, even though father lost an important business association because of it. 'I wouldn't be associated with such a man,' mother said, 'Muggs could read him like a book.'

We used to take turns feeding Muggs to be on his good side, but that didn't always work. He was never in a very good humour, even after a meal. Nobody knew exactly what was the matter with him, but whatever it was it made him irascible, especially in the mornings. Roy never felt very well in the morning, either, especially before breakfast, and once when he came downstairs and found that Muggs had moodily chewed up the morning paper he hit him in the face with a grapefruit and then jumped up on the dining room table, scattering dishes and silverware and spilling

the coffee. Muggs' first free leap carried him all the way across the
table and into a brass fire screen infront of the gas grate but he was
back on his feet in a moment and in the end he got Roy and gave
him a pretty vicious bite in the leg. Then he was all over it; he
never bit anyone more than once at a time. Mother always mentioned that as an argument in his favour; she said he had a quick
temper but that he didn't hold a grudge. She was forever defending
him. I think she liked him because he wasn't well. 'He's not
strong,' she would say, pityingly, but that was inaccurate; he may
not have been well but he was terribly strong.

Nobody knew exactly what was the matter with him

One time my mother went to the Chittenden Hotel to call on a
woman mental healer who was lecturing in Columbus on the
subject of 'Harmonious Vibrations.' She wanted to find out if it
was possible to get harmonious vibrations into a dog. 'He's a large
tan-coloured Airedale,' mother explained. The woman said that
she had never treated a dog but she advised my mother to hold the
thought that he did not bite and would not bite. Mother was
holding the thought the very next morning when Muggs got the
iceman but she blamed that slip-up on the iceman. 'If you didn't
think he would bite you, he wouldn't,' mother told him. He
stomped out of the house in a terrible jangle of vibrations.

One morning when Muggs bit me slightly, more or less in passing, I reached down and grabbed his short stumpy tail and hoisted him into the air. It was a foolhardy thing to do and the last time I saw my mother, about six months ago, she said she didn't know what possessed me. I don't either, except that I was pretty mad. As long as I held the dog off the floor by his tail he couldn't get at me, but he twisted and jerked so, snarling all the time, that I realised I couldn't hold him that way very long. I carried him to the kitchen and flung him onto the floor and shut the door on him just as he crashed against it. But I forgot about the backstairs. Muggs went up the backstairs and down the frontstairs and had me cornered in the living room. I managed to get up onto the mantel-piece above the fireplace, but it gave way and came down with a tremendous crash throwing a large marble clock, several vases, and myself heavily to the floor. Muggs was so alarmed by the racket that when I picked myself up he had disappeared. We couldn't find him anywhere, although we whistled and shouted, until old Mrs Detweiler called after dinner that night. Muggs had bitten her once, in the leg, and she came into the living room only after we assured her that Muggs had run away. She had just seated herself when, with a great growling and scratching of claws, Muggs emerged from under the davenport where he had been quietly hiding all the time, and bit her again. Mother examined the bite and put arnica on it and told Mrs Detweiler that it was only a bruise. 'He just bumped you,' she said. But Mrs Detweiler left the house in a nasty state of mind.

Lots of people reported our Airedale to the police but my father held a municipal office at the time and was on friendly terms with the police. Even so, the cops had been out a couple of times – once when Muggs bit Mrs Rufus Sturtevant and again when he bit Lieutenant-Governor Malloy – but mother told them that it hadn't been Muggs' fault but the fault of the people who were bitten. 'When he starts for them, they scream,' she explained, 'and that excites him.' The cops suggested that it might be a good idea to tie the dog up, but mother said that it mortified him to be tied up and that he wouldn't eat when he was tied up.

Muggs at his meals was an unusual sight. Because of the fact that if you reached toward the floor he would bite you, we usually put his food plate on top of an old kitchen table with a bench alongside the table. Muggs would stand on the bench and eat. I remember that my mother's Uncle Horatio, who boasted that he was the third man up Missionary Ridge, was splutteringly indig-

Lots of people reported our dog to the police

nant when he found out that we fed the dog on a table because we were afraid to put his plate on the floor. He said he wasn't afraid of any dog that ever lived and that he would put the dog's plate on the floor if we would give it to him. Roy said that if Uncle Horatio had fed Muggs on the ground just before the battle he would have been the first man up Missionary Ridge. Uncle Horatio was furious. 'Bring him in! Bring him in now!' he shouted. 'I'll feed the — on the floor!' Roy was all for giving him a chance, but my father wouldn't hear of it. He said that Muggs had already been fed. 'I'll feed him again!' bawled Uncle Horatio. We had quite a time quieting him.

In his last year Muggs used to spend practically all of his time outdoors. He didn't like to stay in the house for some reason or other — perhaps it held too many unpleasant memories for him. Anyway, it was hard to get him to come in and as a result the garbage man, the iceman, and the laundryman wouldn't come

Muggs at his meals was an unusual sight

near the house. We had to haul the garbage down to the corner,
take the laundry out and bring it back, and meet the iceman a
block from home. After this had gone on for some time we hit on
an ingenious arrangement for getting the dog in the house so that
we could lock him up while the gas meter was read, and so on.
Muggs was afraid of only one thing, an electrical storm. Thunder
and lightning frightened him out of his senses (I think he thought a
storm had broken the day the mantelpiece fell). He would rush
into the house and hide under a bed or in a clothes closet. So we
fixed up a thunder machine out of a long narrow piece of sheet
iron with a wooden handle on one end. Mother would shake this
vigorously when she wanted to get her Muggs into the house. It
made an excellent imitation of thunder, but I suppose it was the
most roundabout system for running a household that was ever
devised. It took a lot out of mother.

A few months before Muggs died, he got to 'seeing things.' He would rise slowly from the floor, growling low, and stalk stiff-legged and menacing toward nothing at all. Sometimes the Thing would be just a little to the right or left of a visitor. Once a Fuller Brush Salesman got hysterics. Muggs came wandering into the room like Hamlet following his father's ghost. His eyes were fixed on a spot just to the left of the Fuller Brush man, who stood it until Muggs was about three slow, creeping paces from him. Then he shouted. Muggs wavered on past him into the hallway grumbling to himself but the Fuller man went on shouting. I think mother had to throw a pan of cold water on him before he stopped. That was the way she used to stop us boys when we got into fights.

Muggs died quite suddenly one night. Mother wanted to bury him in the family lot under a marble stone with some such inscription as 'Flights of angels sing thee to thy rest' but we persuaded her it was against the law. In the end we just put up a smooth board above his grave along a lonely road. On the board I wrote with an indelible pencil 'Cave Canem.' Mother was quite pleased with the simple classic dignity of the old Latin epitaph.

University Days

I passed all the other courses that I took at my University, but I
could never pass botany. This was because all botany students
had to spend several hours a week in a laboratory looking through
a microscope. I never once saw a cell through a microscope. This
used to enrage my instructor. He would wander around the
laboratory pleased with the progress all the students were making
in drawing the involved and, so I am told, interesting structure of
flower cells, until he came to me. I would just be standing there. 'I
can't see anything,' I would say. He would begin patiently
enough, explaining how anybody can see through a microscope,
but he would always end up in a fury, claiming that I could *too* see
through a microscope but just pretended that I couldn't. 'It takes
away from the beauty of flowers anyway,' I used to tell him. 'We
are not concerned with beauty in this course,' he would say. 'We
are concerned solely with what I may call the *mechanics* of flars.'
'Well,' I'd say, 'I can't see anything.' 'Try it just once again,' he'd
say, and I would put my eye to the microscope and see nothing at
all, except now and again a nebulous milky substance – a
phenomenon of maladjustment. You were supposed to see a
vivid, restless clockwork of sharply defined plant cells. 'I see what
looks like a lot of milk,' I would tell him. This, he claimed, was the
result of my not having adjusted the microscope properly, so he
would readjust it for me, or rather, for himself. And I would look
again and see milk.

I finally took a deferred pass, as they called it, and waited a year
and tried again. (You had to pass one of the biological sciences or
you couldn't graduate.) The professor had come back from vacation brown as a berry, bright-eyed, and eager to explain cell-
structure again to his classes. 'Well,' he said to me, cheerily, when
we met in the first laboratory hour of the semester, 'we're going to
see cells this time, aren't we?' 'Yes, sir,' I said. Students to right of
me and to left of me and in front of me were seeing cells; what's
more, they were quietly drawing pictures of them in their
notebooks. Of course, I didn't see anything.

'We'll try it,' the professor said to me, grimly, 'with every
adjustment of the microscope known to man. As God is my
witness, I'll arrange this glass so that you see cells through it or I'll
give up teaching. In twenty-two years of botany, I—' He cut off
abruptly for he was beginning to quiver all over, like Lionel

He was beginning to quiver all over like Lionel Barrymore

Barrymore, and he genuinely wished to hold onto his temper; his scenes with me had taken a great deal out of him.

So we tried it with every adjustment of the microscope known to man. With only one of them did I see anything but blackness or the familiar lacteal opacity, and that time I saw, to my pleasure and amazement, a variegated constellation of flecks, specks, and dots. These I hastily drew. The instructor, noting my activity, came back from an adjoining desk, a smile on his lips and his eyebrows high in hope. He looked at my cell drawing. 'What's that?' he demanded, with a hint of a squeal in his voice. 'That's what I saw,' I said. 'You didn't, you didn't, you *didn*'t!' he screamed, losing control of his temper instantly, and he bent over and squinted into the microscope. His head snapped up. 'That's your eye!' he shouted. 'You've fixed the lens so that it reflects! You've drawn your eye!'

Another course that I didn't like, but somehow managed to pass, was economics. I went to that class straight from the botany class, which didn't help me any in understanding either subject. I used to get them mixed up. But not as mixed up as another student in my economics class who came there direct from a physics laboratory. He was a tackle on the football team, named Bolenciecwcz. At that time Ohio State University had one of the best football teams in the country, and Bolenciecwcz was one of its outstanding stars. In order to be eligible to play it was necessary for him to keep up in his studies, a very difficult matter, for while he was not dumber than an ox he was not any smarter. Most of his professors were lenient and helped him along. None gave him more hints, in answering questions, or asked him simpler ones than the economics professor, a thin, timid man named Bassum. One day when we were on the subject of transportation and distribution, it came Bolenciecwcz's turn to answer a question. 'Name one means of transportation,' the professor said to him. No light came into the big tackle's eyes. 'Just any means of transportation,' said the professor. Bolenciecwcz sat staring at him. 'That is', pursued the professor, 'any medium, agency, or method of going from one place to another.' Bolenciecwcz had the look of a man who is being led into a trap. 'You may choose among steam, horse-drawn, or electrically propelled vehicles,' said the instructor. 'I might suggest the one which we commonly take in making long journeys across land.' There was a profound silence in which everybody stirred uneasily, including Bolenciecwcz and Mr Bassum. Mr Bassum abruptly broke this silence in an amazing manner. 'Choo-choo-choo,' he said, in a low voice, and turned instantly scarlet. He glanced appealingly around the room. All of us, of course, shared Mr Bassum's desire that Bolenciecwcz should stay abreast of the class in economics, for the Illinois game, one of the hardest and most important of the season, was only a week off. 'Toot, toot, too-toooooooot!' some student with a deep voice moaned, and we all looked encouragingly at Bolenciecwcz. Somebody else gave a fine imitation of a locomotive letting off steam. Mr Bassum himself rounded off the little show. 'Ding, dong, ding, dong,' he said, hopefully. Bolenciecwcz was staring at the floor now, trying to think, his great brow furrowed, his huge hands rubbing together, his face red.

'How did you come to college this year, Mr Bolenciecwcz?' asked the professor. 'Chuffa chuffa, chuffa chuffa.'

'M'father sent me,' said the football player.

'What on?' asked Bassum.

'I git an 'lowance,' said the tackle, in a low, husky voice, obviously embarrassed.

'No, no,' said Bassum. 'Name a means of transportation. What did you *ride* here on?'

'Train,' said Bolenciecwcz.

'Quite right,' said the professor. 'Now, Mr Nugent, will you tell us——'

If I went through anguish in botany and economics – for different reasons – gymnasium work was even worse. I don't even like to think about it. They wouldn't let you play games or join in the exercises with your glasses on and I couldn't see with mine off. I bumped into professors, horizontal bars, agricultural students, and swinging iron rings. Not being able to see, I could take it but I couldn't dish it out. Also, in order to pass gymnasium (and you had to pass it to graduate) you had to learn to swim if you didn't know how. I didn't like the swimming pool, I didn't like swimming, and I didn't like the swimming instructor, and after all these years I still don't. I never swam but I passed my gym work anyway, by having another student give my gymnasium number (978) and swim across the pool in my place. He was a quiet, amiable blonde youth, number 473, and he would have seen through a microscope for me if we could have got away with it, but we couldn't get away with it. Another thing I didn't like about gymnasium work was that they made you strip the day you registered. It is impossible for me to be happy when I am stripped and being asked a lot of questions. Still, I did better than a lanky agricultural student

Bolenciecwcz was trying to think

who was cross-examined just before I was. They asked each student what college he was in – that is, whether Arts, Engineering, Commerce, or Agriculture. 'What college are you in?' the instructor snapped at the youth in front of me. 'Ohio-State University,' he said promptly.

It wasn't that agricultural student but it was another a whole lot like him who decided to take up journalism, possibly on the ground that when farming went to hell he could fall back on newspaper work. He didn't realise, of course, that that would be very much like falling back full-length on a kit of carpenter's tools. Haskins didn't seem cut out for journalism, being too embarrassed to talk to anybody and unable to use a typewriter, but the editor of the college paper assigned him to the cow barns, the sheep house, the horse pavillion, and the animal husbandry department generally. This was a genuinely big 'beat', for it took up five times as much ground and got ten times as great a legislative appropriation as the College of Liberal Arts. The agricultural student knew animals, but nevertheless his stories were dull and colourlessly written. He took all afternoon on each of them, on account of having to hunt for each letter on the typewriter. Once in a while had to ask somebody to help him hunt. 'C' and 'L', in particular, were hard letters for him to find. His editor finally got pretty much annoyed at the farmer-journalist because his pieces were so uninteresting. 'See here, Haskins,' he snapped at him one day, 'Why is it we never have anything hot from you on the horse pavilion? Here we have two hundred head of horses on this campus – more than any other university in the Western Conference except Purdue – and yet you never get any real low down on them. Now shoot over to the horse barns and dig up something lively.' Haskins shambled out and came back in about an hour; he said he had something. 'Well, start it off snappily,' said the editor. 'Something people will read.' Haskins set to work and in a couple of hours brought a sheet of typewritten paper back to the desk; it was a two-hundred word story about some disease that had broken out among the horses. Its opening sentence was simple but arresting. It read: 'Who has noticed the sores on the tops of the horses in the animal husbandry building?'

Ohio State was a land grant university and therefore two years of military drill was compulsory. We drilled with old Springfield rifles and studied the tactics of the Civil War even though the World War was going on at the time. At 11 o'clock each morning thousands of freshmen and sophomores used to deploy over the campus, moodily creeping up on the old chemistry building. It was good training for the kind of warfare that was waged at Shiloh but it had no connection with what was going on in Europe. Some people used to think there was German money behind it, but they didn't dare say so or they would have been thrown in jail as German spies. It was a period of muddy thought and marked, I believe, the decline of higher education in the Middle West.

As a soldier I was never any good at all. Most of the cadets were glumly indifferent soldiers, but I was no good at all. Once General Littlefield, who was commandant of the cadet corps, popped up in front of me during regimental drill and snapped, 'You are the main trouble with this university!' I think he meant that my type was the main trouble with the university but he may have meant me individually. I was mediocre at drill, certainly – that is, until my senior year. By that time I had drilled longer than anybody else in the Western Conference, having failed at military at the end of each preceding year so that I had to do it all over again. I was the only senior still in uniform. The uniform which, when new, had made me look like an inter-urban railway conductor, now that it had become faded and too tight made me look like Bert Williams in his bellboy act. This had a definitely bad effect on my morale. Even so, I had become by sheer practise little short of wonderful at squad manoeuvres.

One day General Littlefield picked our company out of the whole regiment and tried to get it mixed up by putting it through one movement after another as fast as we could execute them: squads right, squads left, squads on right into line, squads right about, squads left front into line etc. In about three minutes one hundred and nine men were marching in one direction and I was marching away from them at an angle of forty degrees, all alone. 'Company, halt!' shouted General Littlefield, 'That man is the only man who has it right!' I was made a corporal for my achievement.

The next day General Littlefield summoned me to his office. He was swatting flies when I went in. I was silent and he was silent too, for a long time. I don't think he remembered me or why he had sent for me, but he didn't want to admit it. He swatted some more flies, keeping his eyes on them narrowly before he let go with the swatter. 'Button up your coat!' he snapped. Looking back on it now I can see that he meant me although he was looking at a fly, but I just stood there. Another fly came to rest on a paper in front of the general and began rubbing its hind legs together. The general lifted the swatter cautiously. I moved restlessly and the fly flew away. 'You startled him!' barked General Littlefield, looking at me severely. I said I was sorry. 'That won't help the situation!' snapped the General, with cold military logic. I didn't see what I could do except offer to chase some more flies toward his desk, but I didn't say anything. He stared out the window at the faraway figures of co-eds crossing the campus toward the library. Finally, he told me I could go. So I went. He either didn't know which cadet I was or else he forgot what he wanted to see me about. It may have been that he wished to apologise for having called me the main trouble with the university; or maybe he had decided to compliment me on my brilliant drilling of the day before and then at the last minute decided not to. I don't know. I don't think about it much any more.

Draft Board Nights

I left the University in June, 1918, but I couldn't get into the army on account of my sight, just as grandfather couldn't get in on account of his age. He applied several times and each time he took off his coat and threatened to whip the men who said he was too old. The disappointment of not getting to Germany (he saw no sense in everybody going to France) and the strain of running around town seeing influential officials finally got him down in bed. He had wanted to lead a division and his chagrin at not being able to enlist as a private was too much for him. His brother Jake, some fifteen years younger than he was, sat up at night with him after he took to bed, because we were afraid he might leave the house without even putting on his clothes. Grandfather was against the idea of Jake watching over him — he thought it was a lot of tomfoolery — but Jake hadn't been able to sleep at night for twenty-eight years, so he was the perfect person for such a vigil.

On the third night, grandfather was wakeful. He would open his eyes, look at Jake, and close them again, frowning. He never answered any question Jake asked him. About four o'clock that morning, he caught his brother sound asleep in the big leather chair beside the bed. When once Jake did fall asleep he slept deeply, so that grandfather was able to get up, dress himself, undress Jake, and put him in bed without waking him. When my Aunt Florence came into the room at seven o'clock, grandfather was sitting in the chair reading the *Memoirs of U.S. Grant* and Jake was sleeping in the bed. 'He watched while I slept,' said grandfather, 'so now I'm watchin' while he sleeps.' It seemed fair enough.

One reason we didn't want grandfather to roam around at night was that he had said something once or twice about going over to Lancaster, his old home town, and putting his problem up to 'Cump' — that is, General William Tecumseh Sherman, also an old Lancaster boy. We knew that his inability to find Sherman would be bad for him and we were afraid that he might try to get there in the little electric runabout that had been bought for my grandmother. She had become, surprisingly enough, quite skilful at getting around town in it. Grandfather was astonished and a little

About four o'clock he caught his brother asleep

indignant when he saw her get into the contraption and drive off smoothly and easily. It was her first vehicular triumph over him in almost fifty years of married life and he determined to learn to drive the thing himself. A famous old horseman, he approached it as he might have approached a wild colt. His brow would darken and he would begin to curse. He always leaped into it quickly, as if it might pull out from under him if he didn't get into the seat fast enough. The first few times he tried to run the electric, he went swiftly around in a small circle, drove over the curb, across the sidewalk, and up, onto the lawn. We all tried to persuade him to give up, but his spirit was aroused. 'Git that goddam buggy back in the road!' he would say, imperiously. So we would manœuvre it back into the street and he would try again. Pulling too savagely on the guiding-bar – to teach the electric a lesson – was what took him around in a circle, and it was difficult to make him understand that it was best to relax and not get mad. He had the notion that if you didn't hold her, she would throw you. And a man who (or so he often told us) had driven a four-horse McCormick reaper when he was five years old did not intend to be thrown by an electric runabout.

Since there was no way of getting him to give up learning to operate the electric, we would take him out to Franklin Park, where the roadways were wide and unfrequented, and spend an hour or so trying to explain the differences between driving a horse and carriage and driving an electric. He would keep muttering all the time; he never got it out of his head that when he took the driver's seat the machine flattened its ears on him, so to speak. After a few weeks, nevertheless, he got so he could run the electric for a hundred yards or so along a fairly straight line. But whenever he took a curve, he invariably pulled or pushed the bar too quickly and too hard and headed for a tree or a flower bed. Someone was always with him and we would never let him take the car out of the park.

One morning when grandmother was all ready to go to market, she called the garage and told them to send the electric around. They said that grandfather had already been there and taken it out. There was a tremendous to-do. We telephoned Uncle Will and he got out his Lozier and we started off to hunt for grandfather. It was not yet seven o'clock and there was fortunately little traffic. We headed for Franklin Park, figuring that he might have gone out there to try to break the car's spirit. One or two early pedestrians had seen a tall old gentleman with a white beard driving a little electric and cussing as he drove. We followed a tortuous trail and found them finally on Nelson Road, about four miles from the town of Shepard. Grandfather was standing in the road shouting, and the back wheels of the electric were deeply entangled in a barbed-wire fence. Two workmen and a farmhand were trying to get the thing loose. Grandfather was in a state of high wrath about the electric. 'The ——— ——— ——— backed up on me!' he told us.

But to get back to the war. The Columbus draft board never called grandfather for service, which was a lucky thing for them because they would have had to take him. There were stories that several old men of eighty or ninety had been summoned in the confusion, but somehow or other grandfather was missed. He waited every day for the call, but it never came. My own experience was quite different. I was called almost every week, even though I had been exempted from service the first time I went

There was a tremendous to-do

before the medical examiners. Either they were never convinced that it was me or else there was some clerical error in the records which was never cleared up. Anyway, there was usually a letter for me on Monday ordering me to report for examination on the second floor of Memorial Hall the following Wednesday at 9 P.M. The second time I went up I tried to explain to one of the doctors that I had already been exempted. 'You're just a blur to me,' I said, taking off my glasses. 'You're absolutely nothing to me,' he snapped, sharply.

   I had to take off all my clothes each time and jog around the hall with a lot of porters and bank presidents' sons and clerks and poets. Our hearts and lungs would be examined, and then our feet; and finally our eyes. That always came last. When the eye specialist got around to me, he would always say, 'Why, you couldn't get into the service with sight like that!' 'I know,' I would say. Then a week or two later I would be summoned again and go through the same rigmarole. The ninth or tenth time I was called, I happened to pick up one of several stethoscopes that were lying on a table and suddenly, instead of finding myself in the line of draft men, I found myself in the line of examiners 'Hello, doctor,'

said one of them, nodding. 'Hello,' I said. That, of course, was
before I took my clothes off, I might have managed it naked, but I
doubt it. I was assigned, or rather drifted, to the chest-and-lung
section, where I began to examine every other man, thus cutting
old Dr Ridgeway's work in two. 'I'm glad to have you here,
doctor,' he said.

I passed most of the men that came to me, but now and then I
would exempt one just to be on the safe side. I began by making
each of them hold his breath and then say 'mi, mi, mi, mi,' until I
noticed Ridgeway looking at me curiously. He, I discovered,
simply made them say 'ah,' and sometimes he didn't make them
say anything. Once I got hold of a man who, it came out later, had
swallowed a watch – to make the doctors believe there was
something wrong with him inside (it was a common subterfuge:
men swallowed nails, hairpins, ink, etc., in an effort to be let out).
Since I didn't know what you were supposed to hear through a
stethoscope, the ticking of the watch at first didn't surprise me, but
I decided to call Dr Ridgeway into consultation, because nobody
else had ticked. 'This man seems to tick,' I said to him. He looked
at me in surprise but didn't say anything. Then he thumped the
man, laid his ear to his chest, and finally tried the stethoscope.
'Sound as a dollar,' he said. 'Listen lower down,' I told him. The
man indicated his stomach. Ridgeway gave him a haughty, indignant look. 'That is for the abdominal men to worry about,' he said,
and moved off. A few minutes later, Dr Blythe Ballomy got around
to the man and listened, but he didn't blink an eye; his grim
expression never changed. 'You have swallowed a watch, my
man,' he said, crisply. The draftee reddened in embarrassment
and uncertainty. 'On *purpose*?' he asked. 'That I can't say,' the
doctor told him, and went on.

I served with the draft board for about four months. Until the
summonses ceased, I couldn't leave town and as long as I stayed
and appeared promptly for examination, even though I did the
examining, I felt that technically I could not be convicted of
evasion. During the daytime, I worked as publicity agent for an
amusement park, the manager of which was a tall, unexpected
young man named Byron Landis. Some years before, he had
dynamited the men's lounge in the statehouse annex for a prank:
he enjoyed pouring buckets of water on sleeping persons, and
once he had barely escaped arrest for jumping off the top of the
old Columbus Transfer Company building with a homemade
parachute.

An abdominal man worrying

He asked me one morning if I would like to take a ride in the new Scarlet Tornado, a steep and wavy roller-coaster. I didn't want to but I was afraid he would think I was afraid, so I went along. It was about ten o'clock and there was nobody at the park except workmen and attendants and concessionaires in their shirtsleeves. We climbed into one of the long gondolas of the roller-coaster and while I was looking around for the man who was going to run it, we began to move off. Landis, I discovered was running it himself. But it was too late to get out; we had begun to climb, clickety-clockety, up the first steep incline, down the other side of which we careened at eighty miles an hour. 'I didn't know you could run this thing!' I bawled at my companion, as we catapulted up a sixty-degree arch and looped headlong into space. 'I didn't either!' he bawled back. The racket and the rush of air were terrific as we roared into the pitch-black Cave of Darkness and came out and down Monohan's Leap, so called because a workman named Monohan had been forced to jump from it when caught between two approaching experimental cars while it was being completed. That trip, although it ended safely, made a lasting impression on me. It is not too much to say that it has flavoured my life. It is the reason I shout in my sleep, refuse to ride on the elevated, keep jerking the emergency brake in cars other people are driving, have the sensation of flying like a bird when I first lie down, and in certain months can't keep anything on my stomach.

During my last few trips to the draft board, I went again as a draft prospect, having grown tired of being an examiner. None of the doctors who had been my colleagues for so long recognised me,

not even Dr Ridgeway. When he examined my chest for the last time, I asked him if there hadn't been another doctor helping him. He said there had been. 'Did he look anything like me?' I asked. Dr Ridgeway looked at me. 'I don't think so he said, 'he was taller.' (I had my shoes off while he was examining me.) 'A good pulmonary man,' added Ridgeway. 'Relative of yours?' I said yes. He sent me on to Dr Quimby, the specialist who had examined my eyes twelve of fifteen times before. He gave me some simple reading tests. 'You could never get into the army with eyes like that,' he said. 'I know,' I told him.

Late one morning, shortly after my last examination, I was awakened by the sound of bells ringing and whistles blowing. It grew louder and more insistent and wilder. It was the Armistice.

A Note at the End

The hard times of my middle years I pass over, leaving the ringing
bells of 1918, with all their false promise, to mark the end of a
special sequence. The sharp edges of old reticences are softened
in the autobiographer by the passing of time – a man does not pull
the pillow over his head when he wakes in the morning because
he suddenly remembers some awful thing that happened to him
fifteen or twenty years ago, but the confusions and the panics of
last year and the year before are too close for contentment. Until a
man can quit talking loudly to himself in order to shout down the
memories of blunderings and gropings, he is in no shape for the
painstaking examination of distress and the careful ordering of
event so necessary to a calm and balanced exposition of what,
exactly, was the matter. The time I fell out of the gun room in Mr
James Stanley's house in Green Lake, New York, is for instance,
much too near for me to go into with any peace of mind, although
it happened in 1925, the ill-fated year of 'Horses, Horses, Horses'
and 'Valencia.' There is now, I understand, a porch to walk out
onto when you open the door I opened that night, but there wasn't
then.

They tried to sell me baskets

A hotel room in Louisville

The mistaken exits and entrances of my thirties have moved me several times to some thought of spending the rest of my days wandering aimlessly around the South Seas, like a character out of Conrad, silent and inscrutable. But the necessity for frequent visits to my oculist and dentist has prevented this. You can't be running back from Singapore every few months to get your lenses changed and still retain the proper mood for wandering. Furthermore, my horn-rimmed glasses and my Ohio accent betray me, even when I sit on the terraces of little tropical cafes, wearing a pith helmet, staring straight ahead, and twitching a muscle in my jaw. I found this out when I tried wandering around the West Indies one summer. Instead of being followed by the whispers of men and the glances of women, I was followed by bead salesmen and native women with postcards. Nor did any dark girl, looking at all like Tondelaya in 'White Cargo,' come forward and offer to go to pieces with me. They tried to sell me baskets.

Under these circumstances it is impossible to be inscrutable and a wanderer who isn't inscrutable might just as well be back at Broad and High Streets in Columbus sitting in the Baltimore Dairy

Lunch. Nobody from Columbus has ever made a first rate wanderer in the Conradean tradition. Some of them have been fairly
good at disappearing for a few days to turn up in a hotel in
Louisville with a bad headache and no recollection of how they
got there, but they always scurry back to their wives with some
cock-and-bull story of having lost their memory or having gone
away to attend the annual convention of the Fraternal Order of
Eagles.

There was, of course, even for Conrad's Lord Jim, no running
away. The cloud of his special discomfiture followed him like a
pup, no matter what ships he took or what wildernesses he
entered. In the pathways between office and home and home and
houses of settled people there are always, ready to snap at you, the
little perils of routine living, but there is no escape in the unplanned tangent, the sudden turn. In Martinique, when the whistle
blew for the tourists to get back on the ship, I had a quick, wild,
and lovely moment when I decided I wouldn't get back on the
ship. I did, though. And I found that somebody had stolen the
pants to my dinner jacket.

The Departure of Emma Inch

Emma Inch looked no different from any other middle-aged, thin woman you might glance at in the subway or deal with across the counter of some small store in a country town, and then forget forever. Her hair was drab and unabundant, her face made no impression on you, her voice I don't remember – it was just a voice. She came to us with a letter of recommendation from some acquaintance who knew that we were going to Martha's Vineyard for the summer and wanted a cook. We took her because there was nobody else, and she seemed all right. She had arrived at our hotel in Forty-fifth Street the day before we were going to leave and we got her a room for the night, because she lived way uptown somewhere. She said she really ought to go back and give up her room, but I told her I'd fix that.

Emma Inch had a big scuffed brown suitcase with her, and a Boston bull terrier. His name was Feely. Feely was seventeen years old and he grumbled and growled and snuffled all the time, but we needed a cook and we agreed to take Feely along with Emma Inch, if she would take care of him and keep him out of the way. It turned out to be easy to keep Feely out of the way because he would lie grousing anywhere Emma put him until she came and picked him up again. I never saw him walk. Emma had owned him, she said, since he was a pup. He was all she had in the world, she told us, with a mist in her eyes. I felt embarrassed but not touched. I didn't see how anybody could love Feely.

I didn't lose any sleep about Emma Inch and Feely the night of the day they arrived, but my wife did. She told me next morning that she had lain awake a long time thinking about the cook and her dog, because she felt kind of funny about them. She didn't know why. She just had a feeling that they were kind of funny. When we were all ready to leave – it was about three o'clock in the afternoon, for we had kept putting off the packing – I phoned Emma's room, but she didn't answer. It was getting late and we felt nervous – the Fall River boat would sail in about two hours. We couldn't understand why we hadn't heard anything from Emma and Feely. It wasn't until four o'clock that we did. There was a small rap on the door of our bedroom and I opened it and Emma

and Feely were there, Feely in her arms, snuffing and snaffling, as if he had been swimming a long way.

My wife told Emma to get her bag packed, we were leaving in a little while. Emma said her bag *was* packed, except for her electric fan, and she couldn't get that in. 'You won't need an electric fan at the Vineyard,' my wife told her. 'It's cool there, even during the day, and it's almost cold at night. Besides, there is no electricity in the cottage we are going to.' Emma Inch seemed distressed. She studied my wife's face. 'I'll have to think of something else then,' she said. 'Mebbe I could let the water run all night.' We both sat down and looked at her. Feely's asthmatic noises were the only sounds in the room for a while. 'Doesn't that dog ever stop that?' I asked, irritably. 'Oh, he's just talking,' said Emma. 'He talks all the time, but I'll keep him in my room and he won't bother you none.' 'Doesn't he bother you?' I asked. 'He *would* bother me,' said Emma, 'at night, but I put the electric fan on and keep the light burning. He don't make so much noise when it's light, because he don't snore. The fan kind of keeps me from noticing him. I put a piece of cardboard, like, where the fan hits it and then I don't notice Feely so much. Mebbe I could let the water run in my room all night instead of the fan.' I said 'Hmmm' and got up and mixed a drink for my wife and me – we had decided not to have one till we got on the boat, but I thought we'd better have one now. My wife didn't tell Emma there would be no running water in her room at the Vineyard.

'We've been worried about you, Emma,' I said. 'I phoned your room but you didn't answer.' 'I never answer the phone', said Emma, 'because I always get a shock. I wasn't there anyways. I couldn't sleep in that room. I went back to Mrs McCoy's on Seventy-eighth Street.' I lowered my glass. 'You went back to Seventy-eighth Street last *night*?' I demanded. 'Yes, sir,' she said. 'I had to tell Mrs McCoy I was going away and woundn't be there any more for a while – Mrs McCoy's the landlady. Anyways, I never sleep in a hotel.' She looked around the room. 'They burn down,' she told us.

It came out that Emma Inch had not only gone back to Seventy-eighth Street the night before but had walked all the way, carrying Feely. It had taken her an hour or two, because Feely didn't like to be carried very far at a time, so she had had to stop every block or so and put him down on the sidewalk for a while. It had taken her just as long to walk back to our hotel, too; Feely, it seems, never got up before afternoon – that's why she was so late. She was sorry. My wife and I finished our drinks, looking at each other, and at Feely.

Emma Inch didn't like the idea of riding to Pier 14 in a taxi, but after ten minutes of cajoling and pleading she finally got in. 'Make it go slow,' she said. We had enough time, so I asked the driver to take it easy. Emma kept getting to her feet and I kept pulling her back onto the seat. 'I never been in an automobile before,' she said. 'It goes awful fast.' Now and then she gave a little squeal of fright. The driver turned his head and grinned. 'You're O.K. wit' me, lady,' he said. Feely growled at him. Emma waited until he had turned away again, and then she leaned over to my wife and whispered. 'They all take cocaine,' she said. Feely began to make a new sound – a kind of high, agonised yelp. 'He's singing,' said Emma. She gave a strange little giggle, but the expression of her face didn't change. 'I wish you had put the Scotch where we could get at it,' said my wife.

If Emma Inch had been afraid of the taxicab, she was terrified by the *Priscilla* of the Fall River Line. 'I don't think I can go,' said Emma. 'I don't think I could get on a boat. I didn't know they were so big.' She stood rooted to the pier, clasping Feely. She must have squeezed him too hard, for he screamed – he screamed like a woman. We all jumped. 'It's his ears,' said Emma. 'His ears hurt.' We finally got her on the boat, and once aboard, in the salon, her terror abated somewhat. Then the three parting blasts of the boat whistle rocked lower Manhattan. Emma Inch leaped to her feet and began to run, letting go of her suitcase (which she had refused to give up to a porter) but holding onto Feely. I caught her just as she reached the gangplank. The ship was on its way when I let go of her arm.

It was a long time before I could get Emma to go to her stateroom, but she went at last. It was an inside stateroom, and she didn't seem to mind it. I think she was surprised to find that it was like a room, and had a bed and a chair and a washbowl. She put Feely down on the floor. 'I think you'll have to do something about the dog,' I said. 'I think they put them somewhere and you get them when you get off.' 'No, they don't,' said Emma. I guess, in this case, they didn't. I don't know. I shut the door on Emma Inch and Feely, and went away. My wife was drinking straight Scotch when I got to our stateroom.

The next morning, cold and early, we got Emma and Feely off the *Priscilla* at Fall River and over to New Bedford in a taxi and onto the little boat for Martha's Vineyard. Each move was as difficult as getting a combative drunken man out of the night club in which he fancies he has been insulted. Emma sat in a chair on the Vineyard boat, as far away from sight of the water as she could get, and closed her eyes and held onto Feely. She had thrown a coat over Feely, not only to keep him warm but to prevent any of the ship's officers from taking him away from her. I went in from the deck at intervals to see how she was. She was all right, or at least all right for her, until five minutes before the boat reached the dock at Woods Hole, the only stop between New Bedford and the Vineyard. Then Feely got sick. Or at any rate Emma said he was sick. He didn't seem to me any different from what he always was – his breathing was just as abnormal and irregular. But Emma said he was sick. There were tears in her eyes. 'He's a very sick dog, Mr Thurman,' she said. 'I'll have to take him home.' I knew by the way she said 'home' what she meant. She meant Seventy-eighth Street.

The boat tied up at Woods Hole and was motionless and we could hear the racket of the deckhands on the dock loading freight. 'I'll get off here,' said Emma, firmly, or with more firmness, anyway, than she had shown yet. I explained to her that we would be home in half an hour, that everything would be fine then, everything would be wonderful. I said Feely would be a new dog. I told her people sent sick dogs to Martha's Vineyard to be cured. But it was no good. 'I'll have to take him off here,' said Emma. 'I always have to take him home when he is sick.' I talked to her eloquently about the loveliness of Martha's Vineyard and the nice houses and the nice people and the wonderful accommodations for dogs. But I knew it was useless. I could tell by looking at her. She was going to get off the boat at Woods Hole.

'You really can't do this,' I said, grimly, shaking her arm. Feely snarled weakly. 'You haven't any money and you don't know where you are. You're a long way from New York. Nobody ever got from Woods Hole to New York alone.' She didn't seem to hear me. She began walking toward the stairs leading to the gangplank, crooning to Feely. 'You'll have to go all the way back on boats', I said, 'or else take a train, and you haven't any money. If you are going to be so stupid and leave us now, I can't give you any money.' 'I don't want any money, Mr Thurman,' she said. 'I haven't earned any money.' I walked along in irritable silence for a moment; then I gave her some money. I made her take it. We got to the gangplank. Feely snaffled and gurgled. I saw now that his eyes were a little red and moist. I know it would do no good to summon my wife – not when Feely's health was at stake, 'How do

you expect to get home from here?' I almost shouted at Emma Inch
as she moved down the gangplank. 'You're way out on the end of
Massachusetts.' She stopped and turned around. 'We'll walk,' she
said. 'We like to walk, Feely and me.' I just stood still and watched
her go.

When I went up on deck, the boat was clearing for the Vineyard.
'How's everything?' asked my wife. I waved a hand in the direction of the dock. Emma Inch was standing there, her suitcase at her
feet, her dog under one arm, waving goodbye to us with her free
hand. I had never seen her smile before, but she was smiling now.

The Topaz Cufflinks Mystery

When the motorcycle cop came roaring up, unexpectedly, out of Never-Never Land (the way motorcycle cops do), the man was on his hands and knees in the long grass beside the road, barking like a dog. The woman was driving slowly along in a car that stopped about eighty feet away; its headlights shone on the man: middle-aged, bewildered, sedentary. He got to his feet.

'What's goin' on here?' asked the cop. The woman giggled. 'Cock-eyed,' thought the cop. He did not glance at her.

'I guess it's gone,' said the man. 'I—ah—could not find it.'

'What was it?'

'What I lost?' The man squinted, unhappily. 'Some—some cufflinks; topazes set in gold.' He hesitated: the cop didn't seem to believe him. 'They were the colour of a fine Moselle,' said the man. He put on a pair of spectacles which he had been holding in his hand. The woman giggled.

'Hunt things better with ya glasses off?' asked the cop. He pulled his motorcycle to the side of the road to let a car pass. 'Better pull over off the concrete, lady,' he said. She drove the car off the roadway.

'I'm nearsighted,' said the man. 'I can hunt things at a distance with my glasses on, but I do better with them off if I am close to something.' The cop kicked his heavy boots through the grass where the man had been crouching.

'He was barking,' ventured the lady in the car, 'so that I could see where he was.' The cop pulled his machine up on its standard; he and the man walked over to the automobile.

'What I don't get,' said the officer, 'is how you lose ya cufflinks a hunderd feet in front of where ya car is; a person usually stops his car *past* the place he loses somethin', not a hunderd feet before he gits *to* the place.'

The lady laughed again; her husband got slowly into the car, as if he were afraid the officer would stop him any moment. The officer studied them.

'Been to a party?' he asked. It was after midnight.

'We're not drunk, if that's what you mean,' said the woman, smiling. The cop tapped his fingers on the door of the car

'You people didn't lose no topazes,' he said.

'Is it against the law for a man to be down on all fours beside a road, barking in a perfectly civil manner?' demanded the lady.

'No ma'am,' said the cop. He made no move to get on his motorcycle, however, and go on about his business. There was just the quiet chugging of the cycle engine and the auto engine, for a time.

'I'll tell you how it was, Officer,' said the man, in a crisp, new tone. 'We were settling a bet. O.K.?'

'O.K.,' said the cop. 'Who win?' There was another pulsing silence.

'The lady bet', said her husband, with dignity, as though he were explaining some important phase of industry to a newly hired clerk, 'the lady bet that my eyes would shine like a cat's do at night, if she came upon me suddenly close to the ground alongside the road. We had passed several persons, whose eyes did *not* gleam——'

'Simply because they were above the light and not under it,' said the lady. 'A man's eyes would gleam like a cat's if people were ordinarily caught by headlights at the same angle as cats are.'

The cop walked over to where he had left his motorcycle, picked it up, kicked the standard out, and wheeled it back.

'A cat's eyes', he said, 'are different than yours and mine. Dogs, cats, skunks, it's all the same. They can see in a dark room.'

'Not in a *totally* dark room,' said the lady.

'Yes, they can,' said the cop.

'No, they can't; not if there is no light at all in the room, not if it's absolutely *black*,' said the lady. 'The question came up the other night; there was a professor there and he said there must be at least a ray of light, no matter how faint.'

'That may be,' said the cop, after a solemn pause, pulling at his gloves. 'But people's eyes don't shine — I go along these roads every night an' pass hunderds of cats and hunderds of people.'

'The people are never close to the ground,' said the lady.

'*I* was close to the ground,' said her husband.

'Look at it this way,' said the cop. 'I've seen wildcats in *trees* at night and *their* eyes shine.'

'There you are!' said the lady's husband. 'That proves it.'

'I don't see how,' said the lady. There was another silence.

'Because a wildcat in a tree's eyes are higher than the level of a man's,' said the husband. The cop may possibly have followed this, the lady obviously did not, neither one said anything. The cop got on his machine, raced his engine, seemed to be thinking about something, and throttled down. He turned to the man.

'Took ya glasses off so the headlights wouldn't make ya glasses shine, huh?' he asked.

'That's right,' said the man. The cop waved his hand, triumphantly, and roared away. 'Smart guy,' said the man to his wife, irritably.

'I still don't see where the wildcat proves anything,' said his wife. He drove off slowly.

'Look,' he said. 'You claim that the whole thing depends on how *low* a cat's eyes are; I——'

'I didn't say that; I said it all depends on how *high* a man's eyes . . .'

Mr Pendly and the Poindexter

Mr Pendly hadn't driven the family car for five years, since, to be exact, the night of the twenty-third of October, 1930, when he mistook a pond for a new concrete road and turned off onto it. He didn't really drive into the pond, only hovered at the marge, for Mrs Pendly shut off the ignition and jerked the emergency brake. Mr Pendly was only forty-two, but his eyes weren't what they had been. After that night, Mrs Pendly always drove the car. She even drove it during the daytime, for although Mr Pendly could see in the daytime, his nerve was gone. He was obsessed with the fear that he wouldn't see the traffic lights, or would get them mixed up with lights on storefronts, or would jam on his brakes when postmen blew their whistles. You can't drive toward a body of water thinking it's made of concrete without having your grip on yourself permanently loosened.

Mr Pendly was not particularly unhappy about the actual fact of not driving a car any more. He had never liked to drive much. It galled him slightly that his wife could see better than he could and it gave him a feeling of inferiority to sit mildly beside her while she solved the considerable problems of city traffic. He used to dream at night of descending, in an autogiro, on some garden party she was attending: he would come down in a fine landing, leap out, shout 'Hahya, Bee!,' sweep her into the machine, and zoom away. He used to think of things like that while he was riding with her.

One day Mrs Pendly said she thought they ought to trade in the old car for another one. What she had in mind was a second-hand Poindexter — she was tired of small cars. You could, she said, get perfectly marvellous bargains in 1932 and 1933 Poindexters. Mr Pendly said he supposed you could. He didn't know anything about Poindexters, and very little about any automobile. He knew how to make them go and how to stop them, and how to back up. Mrs Pendly was not good at backing up. When she turned her head and looked behind her, her mind and hands ceased to co-ordinate. It rather pleased Mr Pendly that his wife was not good at backing up. Still, outside of that, she knew more about cars than he ever would. The thought depressed him.

Mrs Pendly went to the Poindexter Sales Company, up near Columbus Circle, one day, spent an hour looking around the various floors with a salesman named Huss, and located finally what she described to her husband that evening as a perfectly lovely bargain. True, it was a '31 model, but a late '31 model and not an early '31 model. Mr Pendly said he didn't think there ever were two models in one year, but she said Mr Huss told her there were, that everybody knew there were, and that you could tell by the radiator cap.

She took Mr Pendly up to the Poindexter place the next after-noon to see the car. They had to wait a long time for Mr Huss. Mr Pendly got restless. All the shining Poindexter 16's in the main showroom seemed to him as big as hook-and-ladders and as terrifying. He worried because he knew Mr Huss would expect him to ask acute technical questions about the car, to complain of this and that. Mr Huss, finding out that Mr Pendly didn't know anything at all about automobiles, would sniff in surprise and disdain. A husband whose wife drove the car!

Mr Huss turned out to be a large, vital man. Mr Pendly was vital enough, but not as large as Mr Huss. Their meeting was not much fun for either one. As they got into an elevator to go to the sixth floor, where the lovely bargain was, Mr Huss kept referring to it as a nice job. The sixth floor was filled with second-hand cars and with mechanics, pounding and buffing and tinkering. Mr Pendly had the same feeling in the presence of mechanics that, as a child, he had had during church sermons: he felt that he was at the mercy of malignant powers beyond his understanding.

When they stood in front of the Poindexter that Mrs Pendly had picked out, Huss said to Mr Pendly: 'Whatta you think of that for a piece of merchandise?' Mr Pendly touched a front fender with his fingers. The salesman waited for him to say something, but he didn't say anything. The only part of a car that Mr Pendly could think of at the moment was the fan belt. He felt it would be silly to ask to see the fan belt. Maybe Poindexters didn't have fan belts. Mr Pendly frowned, opened the back door, and shut it. He noticed the monogram of the previous owner on the door. 'That monogram,' said Mr Pendly, 'would have to come off.' Since it seemed that this was all Mr Pendly had to say, his wife and Mr Huss ignored him and got into an intricate talk about grinding valves, relining brakes, putting in a new battery. Mr Pendly felt the way he used to in school when he hadn't prepared his homework. He waited for an opening to cut in on the conversation and thought he saw one when Mrs Pendly said that she didn't like the car not having a vacuum pump. Mr Pendly jumped to the conclusion that a vacuum pump was something you could buy and put under the back seat, like a fire-extinguisher. 'We could pick up a vacuum pump in any accessory shop,' he said. Both his wife and Mr Huss gave him a surprised look and then went on to the question of the rear tyres.

Mr Pendly wandered sadly over to where a mechanic was lying under a big car. As he got there, the mechanic crawled out from under, jumped up, and brushed against Mr Pendly. 'Look out, Bud,' said the mechanic, who was chewing tobacco. Bud walked back to where his wife and Mr Huss were. He had suddenly thought of the word 'transmission,' and had some idea of asking Mr Huss about that. It occurred to him, however, that maybe free-wheeling had done away with transmission and that he would just be showing his ignorance. Mr Huss was trying to get the luggage compartment at the back of the Poindexter open, because Mrs Pendly said she had to see how large it was. The key wouldn't work. Mr Huss shouted for somebody named Mac, and presently the chewing mechanic walked over. He couldn't open the compartment either, and went away. Mrs Pendly and the salesman walked off to look at the compartment on a similar car, and Mr Pendly set to work. In a few minutes he found out what was the matter. You had to press down on the cover and then turn the key! He had the back open when his wife and Huss returned. They didn't pay any attention to it. They were talking about mileage.

'I got the back open,' said Mr Pendly, finally.

'This was a chauffeur-driven car,' said Mr Huss. 'And it was handled like a watch. There's another hundred thousand miles in it.'

'The front seat would have to be lowered,' said Mrs Pendly. 'I couldn't be stuck way up in the air like that.'

'We'll take care of that,' said Huss. 'that'll be easy.'

'You want to see into the back now?' asked Mr Pendly.

'And you'd be sure to have the brakes tested?' Mrs Pendly said to Huss.

'Those brakes will be A-1 when the job leaves this room,' said Huss. 'We never turn out a piece of merchandise here that isn't A-1.'

Mr Pendly shut the baggage compartment. Then he opened it again. He did this a couple more times.

'Come on, Bert,' his wife said.

On the way home — Mrs Pendly had decided to think the

bargain over, although Huss said somebody else would snap it up if she didn't snap it up – Mr Pendly sat beside his wife in their old car and thought. She prattled along about the Poindexter but he didn't really hear, although now and then he grunted some answer in a monotone. He was imagining that, as he sauntered over to Mac, Mac got out from under the big car he was working on and said: 'Well, it's got me licked.' Mr Pendly smiled. 'Yeah?' he said, slowly removing his coat and vest. He handed them to Mac. Then he crawled under the car, looked the works over coldly, tinkered delicately and expertly with a couple of rods and a piston, tightened a winch gasket, blew softly into a valve, and crawled out again. He put on his coat and vest. 'Try her now,' he said, indifferently, to Mac. Mac tried her. She worked beautifully. The big mechanic turned slowly to Mr Pendly and held out an oily hand. 'Brother,' said Mac, 'I hand it to you. Where did you ev——?'.

'What's the matter; are you in a trance or what?' asked Mrs Pendly, pulling her husband's sleeve. He gave her a cold, superior look.

'Never mind about me,' he said.

The Indian Sign

'Mr Pinwither is doing wonders with the new Cora Allyn letter,' Mrs Bentley told her husband. He winced slightly. Three letters about the old lady hadn't been enough; somebody had had to turn up another one.

'That's fine,' said Mr Bentley, taking off his overcoat and hanging it up in the hall closet.

'It's all about their moving to New Milford – in 1667,' said Mrs Bentley. 'There's nothing new in it, he says, about the Indians.' She seemed disappointed.

'That's fine,' said Mr Bentley again. His wife, on the verge of a new eagerness, apparently didn't hear.

· 'And,' she said, 'Cora learned a new word today!' *This* Cora, Mr Bentley knew, was of course his little daughter. He really meant his 'That's fine' this time. Still, he winced again. He had wanted to name his daughter Rosemary, after a dream. But his wife and all the stern and silly pride of the Allyns had been behind 'Cora.' Since a certain day almost three hundred years ago the first female born into every ramification of the Allyn family had been named Cora: 'After old Cora Cora herself,' as Henry Bentley said at the Comics' Club the night his daughter was born.

The original Cora Allyn, his little girl's great-great-great-great-great-grandmother, had slain nineteen Pequot Indians single-handed in an incredible and dimly authenticated struggle near New London, Connecticut, in 1643, or 1644. The Allyns could never be positive of the year, for the letters bearing upon the incident were almost three centuries old, yellow and brittle and written crisscross, the thrifty and illegible Colonial method of saving postage charges. Two were undated and the date of the other was faded and tricky, like all of the writing in the three priceless heirlooms of the Allyn family. The letters purported to have been written by one Loyal Holgate, supposedly a young divine, and – Bentley had examined them carefully, or as carefully as anyone who was not an Allyn was allowed to – there apparently *were* passages in them about one Cora Allyn's having slain nineteen Indians. Some of the most eminent antiquarians in the country, including Mr Pinwither, had pored over the letters. They had all but one brought out of the vague, faint scrawlings virtually the same story of the early New England lady's heroic deed. The saturnine Murray Kraull had, it is true, doubted that the word 'nineteen' was really 'nineteen' and even that 'Pequots' was 'Pequots.' He had, indeed, gone so far as to suggest that the phrase might be 'no male peacocks,' for which heresy he had practically been hustled out of Mrs Bentley's mother's house. The other experts had all conformed, however to the letter – and the number – of the legend. In Henry Bentley's mind, as in Mr Kraull's, there would always remain a doubt.

Mr Bentley, quietly and in secret, had long been elaborating on his doubt. So far as he had been able to find out, there was no record of a Cora Allyn who had slain nineteen Indians. There had been a rather famous incident in which a band of Pequots killed a Mrs Anne Williamson, a Massachusetts woman who had settled near Stamford, but that was all. Once, to make a dinner topic, he had tossed out timidly to his wife that he had come upon an old history of the state at his office and so far had found in it no reference to any woman who had killed nineteen Indians. Mrs Bentley's quick, indignant look had caused him to mumble the rest of his suspicions into his shirt-front. It was the closest he ever came to expressing openly his feeling in the matter.

'The new letter,' said Mrs Bentley, as they walked into the living-room, 'tells some more about Rockbottom Thraillkill, the minister who established the third church in what is now New Milford. It was called Appasottowams then, or something like that. It is all in Mr Pinwither's report.'

'That's close enough,' said Mr Bentley. He strove to change the subject. 'What did my little girl say today?' he asked.

'Cora? She said "telephone." '

'That's fine,' said Mr Bentley. It was terrible the way he allowed the name Cora to affect him. There were literally hundreds of Coras among his wife's connections. They kept recurring, like leaf blight, among the spreading branches of the Allyn family. And scarcely a day went by but what someone alluded to the first, great Cora. He encountered her glib ghost at all family gatherings, on all holidays, and before, during, and after every family ceremony, such as marriage, birth, christening, divorce, and death.

Mrs Bentley talked about the small excitements of her day during dinner. Her husband affected to listen, and now and then

gave a sympathetic grunt, but he was quietly contemplating that early American heroine who was so damnable intertwined with his life. Supposing that the story about her *were* true? Why be so insistently conscious and so eternally proud of an ancestor who killed nineteen Indians? Her open-mouthed, wild-eyed gestures during the unmatronly ordeal, the awkwardness of her stance, the disarray of her apparel, must have been disturbingly unattractive. The vision of his little daughter's forebear, who up to her great hour had undoubtedly depended rather charmingly upon a sturdy pioneer husband, suddenly learning that she was more than a match for nineteen males affected Henry Bentley dismally; it saddened him to be continually carried back along the rocky, well-forgotten roads of American life to the prophetic figure of Cora Allyn, standing there against the sky, with her match-lock or her hunting knife or her axe handle, so outrageously and significantly triumphant.

Henry had often tried to get a picture of the famous Cora's husband, old Coppice Allyn. There was little mention of him in the frail letters of almost three centuries ago. Old Coppice was rarely mentioned by the Allyns, either; he remained staunch but indistinct, like a figure in the background of a wood-cut. He had cleared away trees, he had built a house, he had dug a well, he had had a touch of brain fever – things like that: no vivid, red, immortal gestures. What must he have thought that April evening (not 'April' but 'apple,' Kraull had made it out) when he came home from the fields to find a new gleam in his wife's eyes and nineteen new corpses under her feet? He must have felt some vague, alarming resentment; he must have realized, however dimly, that this was the beginning of a new weave in the fabric of life in the Colonies. Poor old Coppice!

'I want to show you,' said Mrs Bentley after dinner, 'Mr Pinwither's report. Of course it's just a preliminary. Mother sent it over.'

'That's fine,' said Mr Bentley. He watched his wife go out of the room and tried to be glad that she, at least, was not a Cora; her oldest sister held that honor. That was something. Mr Bentley seized the chance, now that he was alone, to reflect upon his latest clandestine delving into the history of the Connecticut Indians. The Pequots, he had discovered in a book that very aftrenoon, had been woefully incompetent fighters. Some early militarist had written of them that, fighting as they did, they 'couldn't have killed seven people in seven years.' They shot their arrows high into the air: anybody could see them coming and step out of the way. The Colonial militiamen used to pick up the flinted sticks, break them in two, and laugh at their helpless foes. Even when the shafts did get home, they almost never killed; a neckcloth would turn them aside or even, as in the case of one soldier a piece of cheese carried in one's pocket. Poor, pathetic, stupid old Pequots! Brave they had undeniably been, but dumb. Mr Bentley had suddenly a rather kindly feeling for the Pequots. And he had, at the same time, a new, belittling vision of that grand old lady, the first Cora: he saw her leisurely firing through a chink in the wall of her house, taking all afternoon to knock off nineteen Indians who had no chance against her, who stood on the edge of a clearing firing arrows wistfully into the sky until one of the white woman's blunderbuss slugs – a tenpenny nail or a harness buckle – struck them down. If only they had rushed her! If only one of them had been smart enough to light the end of an arrow and stick it burning in the roof of the Allyn house! They would have finished her off fast enough if they had ever got her outside! Mr Bentley's heart beat faster and his eyes blinked brightly.

'What is it!' asked Mrs Bentley, coming back into the room. Her husband looked so eager and pleased, sitting there.

'I was just thinking,' he said.

Mr Pinwither's preliminary report on the new letter was long and dull. Mr Bentley tried to look interested: he knew better than to appear indifferent to any holy relic connected with the Great Cora.

'Cora's had such a day!' said Mrs Bentley, as they were preparing for bed. 'She went to sleep playing with those toy soldiers and Indians her Uncle Bert gave her.' Mr Bentley had one of his vivid pictures of Uncle Bert. 'Um,' he said, and went downstairs to get his aspirin box out of his coat.

Before he went to bed, Mr Bentley stopped in the nursery to have a good-night look at his little sleeping daughter. She lay sweetly with her hands curled above her head. Mr Bentley regarded the little girl with sad eyes. The line of her forehead and the curve of her chin were (or so the Allyns hysterically claimed) the unmistakable sign of the Great Cora, the proof of the child's proud heritage, the latest blaze along the trail. He stood above her, thinking, a long time.

When Mr Bentley went back to the bedroom, it was pitch-dark; his wife had turned out the light. He tiptoed in. He heard her slow, deep breathing. She was sound asleep.

'Henry?' she called suddenly out of the blackness. Surprised, he did not answer.

'Henry!' she said. There was uneasiness and drowsy bewilderment in her voice.

To Henry Bentley, standing there in the darkness, there came a quick, wild urge. He tried to restrain it, and then, abruptly, he gave way to it, with a profound sense of release. Patting the fingers of his right hand rapidly against his open lips, he gave, at the top of his voice, the Pequot war whoop: 'Ah-wah-wah-wah-wah!'

The Private Life of Mr Bidwell

From where she was sitting, Mrs Bidwell could not see her husband, but she had a curious feeling of tension: she knew he was up
to something:

'What are you doing, George?' she demanded, her eyes still on
her book.

'Mm?'

'What's the matter with you?'

'Pahhhhh-hh,' said Mr Bidwell, in a long, pleasurable exhale. 'I
was holding my breath.'

Mrs Bidwell twisted creakingly in her chair and looked at him;
he was sitting behind her in his favourite place under the parch-
ment lamp with the street scene of old New York on it. 'I was just
holding my breath,' he said again.

'Well, please don't do it,' said Mrs Bidwell, and went back to
her book. There was silence for five minutes.

'George!' said Mrs Bidwell.

'Bwaaaaaa,' said Mr Bidwell. 'What?'

'Will you please *stop* that?' she said. 'It makes me nervous.'

'I don't see how that bothers you,' he said. 'Can't I breathe?'

'You can breathe without holding your breath like a goop,' said
Mrs Bidwell. 'Goop' was a word that she was fond of using; she
rather lazily applied it to everything. It annoyed Mr Bidwell.

'Deep breathing,' said Mr Bidwell, in the impatient tone he used
when explaining anything to his wife, 'is good exercise. You ought
to take more exercise.'

'Well, please don't do it around me,' said Mrs Bidwell, turning
again to the pages of Mr Galsworthy.

At the Cowans' party, a week later, the room was full of chattering people when Mrs Bidwell, who was talking to Lida Carroll,
suddenly turned around as if she had been summoned. In a chair
in a far corner of the room, Mr Bidwell was holding his breath. His
chest was expanded, his chin drawn in; there was a strange stare
in his eyes, and his face was slightly empurpled. Mrs Bidwell
moved into the line of his vision and gave him a sharp, penetrating
look. He deflated slowly and looked away.

Later, in the car, after they had driven in silence a mile or more

on the way home, Mrs Bidwell said, 'It seems to me you might at
least have the kindness not to hold your breath in other people's
houses.'

'I wasn't hurting anybody,' said Mr Bidwell.

'You looked silly!' said his wife. 'You looked perfectly crazy!'
She was driving and she began to speed up, as she always did
when excited or angry. 'What do you suppose people thought –
you sitting there all swelled up, with your eyes popping out?'

'I wasn't all swelled up,' he said, angrily.

'You looked like a goop,' she said. The car slowed down,
sighed, and came to a complete, despondent stop.

'We're out of gas,' said Mrs Bidwell. It was bitterly cold and
nastily sleeting. Mr Bidwell took a long, deep breath.

The breathing situation in the Bidwell family reached a critical
point when Mr Bidwell began to inhale in his sleep, slowly, and
exhale with a protracted, growling 'woooooooo.' Mrs Bidwell,
ordinarily a sound sleeper (except on nights when she was sure
burglars were getting in), would wake up and reach over and
shake her husband. 'George!' she would say.

'Hawwwwww,' Mr Bidwell would say, thickly. 'Wahs maa
nah hm?'

After he had turned over and gone back to sleep, Mrs Bidwell would lie awake, thinking.

One morning at breakfast she said, 'George, I'm not going to put up with this another day. If you can't stop blowing up like a grampus, I'm going to leave you.' There was a slight quick lift in Mr Bidwell's heart, but he tried to look surprised and hurt.

'All right,' he said. 'Let's not talk about it.'

Mrs Bidwell buttered another piece of toast. She described to him the way he sounded in his sleep. He read the paper.

With considerable effort, Mr Bidwell kept from inflating his chest for about a week, but one night at the McNally's he hit on the idea of seeing how many seconds he could hold his breath. He was rather bored by the McNally's party, anyway. He began timing himself with his wrist-watch in a remote corner of the living-room. Mrs Bidwell, who was in the kitchen talking children and clothes with Bea McNally, left her abruptly and slipped back into the living-room. She stood quietly behind her husband's chair. He knew she was there, and tried to let out his breath imperceptibly.

'I see you,' she said, in a low, cold tone. Mr Bidwell jumped up.

'Why don't you let me alone?' he demanded.

'Will you please lower your voice?' she said, smiling so that if anyone were looking he wouldn't think the Bidwells were arguing.

'I'm getting pretty damned tired of this,' said Bidwell in a low voice.

'You've ruined my evening!' she whispered.

'You've ruined mine, too!' he whispered back. They knifed each other, from head to stomach, with their eyes.

'Sitting here like a goop, holding your breath,' said Mrs Bidwell. 'People will think you are an idiot.' She laughed, turning to greet a lady who was approaching them.

Mr Bidwell sat in his office the next afternoon, a black, moist afternoon, tapping a pencil on his desk, and scowling. 'All right, then, get out, get out!' he muttered. 'What do I care?' He was visualizing the scene when Mrs Bidwell would walk out on him. After going through it several times, he returned to his work, feeling vaguely contented. He made up his mind to breathe any way he wanted to, no matter what she did. And, having come to this decision, he oddly enough, and quite without effort, lost interest in holding his breath.

Everything went rather smoothly at the Bidwells' for a month or so. Mr Bidwell didn't do anything to annoy his wife beyond leaving his razor on her dressing-table and forgetting to turn out the hall light when he went to bed. Then there came the night of the Bentons' party.

Mr Bidwell, bored as usual, was sitting in a far corner of the room, breathing normally. His wife was talking animatedly with Beth Williamson about negligees. Suddenly her voice slowed and an uneasy look came into her eyes: George was up to something. She turned around and sought him out. To anyone but Mrs Bidwell he must have seemed like any husband sitting in a chair. But his wife's lips set tightly. She walked casually over to him.

'What are you doing?' she demanded.

'Hm?' he said, looking at her vacantly.

'What are you *doing*?' she demanded, again. He gave her a harsh, venomous look, which she returned.

'I'm multiplying numbers in my head,' he said, slowly and evenly, 'if you must know.' In the prolonged, probing examination that they silently, without moving any muscles save those of their eyes, gave each other, it became solidly, frozenly apparent to both of them that the end of their endurance had arrived. The curious bond that held them together snapped – rather more easily than either had supposed was possible. That night, while undressing for bed, Mr Bidwell calmly multiplied numbers in his head. Mrs Bidwell stared coldly at him for a few moments, holding a stocking in her hand; she didn't bother to berate him. He paid no attention to her. The thing was simply over.

George Bidwell lives alone now (his wife remarried). He never goes to parties any more, and his old circle of friends rarely sees him. The last time that any of them did see him, he was walking along a country road with the halting, uncertain gait of a blind man: he was trying to see how many steps he could take without opening his eyes.

The Kerb in the Sky

When Charlie Deshler announced that he was going to marry Dorothy, someone said he would lose his mind posthaste. 'No', said a wit who knew them both, 'post hoc.' Dorothy had begun, when she was quite young, to finish sentences for people. Sometimes she finished them wrongly, which annoyed the person who was speaking, and sometimes she finished them correctly, which annoyed the speaker even more.

'When William Howard Taft was—' some guest in Dorothy's family's home would begin.

'President!' Dorothy would pipe up. The speaker may have meant to say 'President' or he may have meant to say 'young', or 'Chief Justice of the Supreme Court of the United States.' In any case, he would shortly put on his hat and go home. Like most parents, Dorothy's parents did not seem to be conscious that her mannerism was a nuisance. Very likely they thought that it was cute, or even bright. It is even probable that when Dorothy's mother first said 'Come, Dorothy, eat your—' and Dorothy said 'Spinach, dear,' the former telephoned Dorothy's father at the office and told him about it, and he told everybody he met that day about it – and the next day and the day after.

When Dorothy grew up she became quite pretty and so even more of a menace. Gentlemen became attracted to her and then attached to her. Emotionally she stirred them, but mentally she soon began to wear them down. Even in her late teens she began correcting their English. 'Not "was", Arthur', she would say, ' "were." "Were prepared". See?' Most of her admirers tolerated this habit because of their interest in her lovely person, but as time went on and her interest in them remained more instructive than sentimental, they slowly drifted away to less captious, if dumber, girls.

Charlie Deshler, however, was an impetuous man, of the sweep-them-off-their-feet persuasion, and he became engaged to Dorothy so quickly and married her in so short a time that, being deaf to the warnings of friends, whose concern he regarded as mere jealousy, he really didn't know anything about Dorothy except that she was pretty and bright-eyed and (to him) desirable.

Dorothy as a wife came, of course, into her great flowering: she took to correcting Charlie's stories. He had travelled widely and experienced greatly and was a truly excellent *raconteur*. Dorothy was, during their courtship, genuinely interested in him and in his stories, and since she had never shared any of the adventures he told about, she could not know when he made mistakes in time or in place or in identities. Beyond suggesting a change here and there in the number of a verb, she more or less let him alone. Charlie spoke rather good English, anyway – he knew when to say 'were' and when to say 'was' after 'if' – and this was another reason he didn't find Dorothy out.

I didn't call on them for quite a while after they were married, because I liked Charlie and I knew I would feel low if I saw him coming out of the anaesthetic of her charms and beginning to feel the first pains of reality. When I did finally call, conditions were, of course, all that I had feared. Charlie began to tell, at dinner, about a motor trip the two had made to this town and that – I never found out for sure what towns, because Dorothy denied almost every-thing that Charlie said. 'The next day', he would say, 'we got an early start and drove two hundred miles to Fairview—' 'Well,' Dorothy would say, 'I wouldn't call it *early*. It wasn't as early as the first day we set out, when we got up about *seven*. And we only drove a hundred and eighty miles, because I remember looking at that mileage thing when we started.'

'Anyway, when we got to Fairview—' Charlie would go on. But Dorothy would stop him. 'Was it Fairview that day, darling?' she would ask. Dorothy often interrupted Charlie by asking him if he were right, instead of telling him that he was wrong, but it amounted to the same thing, for if he would reply: 'Yes, I'm sure it was Fairview,' she would say: 'But it *wasn't*, darling,' and then go on with the story herself. (She called everybody that she differed from 'darling'.)

Once or twice, when I called on them or they called on me, Dorothy would let Charlie get almost to the climax of some interesting account of a happening and then, like a tackler from behind, throw him just as he was about to cross the goal-line. There is nothing in life more shocking to the nerves and to the mind than this. Some husbands will sit back amiably – almost it seems, proudly – when their wives interrupt, and let them go with the story, but these are beaten husbands. Charlie did not become beaten. But his wife's tackles knocked the wind out of him, and he began to realise that he would have to do something. What he did was rather ingenious. At the end of the second year of their marriage, when you visited the Deshlers, Charlie would begin some outlandish story about a dream he had had, knowing that Dorothy could not correct him on his own dreams. They became the only life he had that was his own.

'I thought I was running an aeroplane', he would say, 'made out of telephone wires and pieces of old leather. I was trying to make it fly to the moon, taking off from my bedroom. About halfway up to the moon, however, a man who looked like Santa Claus, only he was dressed in the uniform of a customs officer, waved at me to stop – he was in a plane made of telephone wires, too. So I pulled over to a cloud. "Here", he said to me, "you can't go to the moon, if you are the man who invented these wedding cookies." Then he showed me a cookie made in the shape of a man and woman being married – little images of a man and a woman and a minister, made of dough and fastened firmly to a round, crisp cookie base.' So he would go on.

Any psychiatrist will tell you that at the end of the way Charlie was going lies madness in the form of monomania. You can't live in a fantastic dream world, night in and night out and then day in and day out, and remain sane. The substance began to die slowly out of Charlie's life, and he began to live entirely in shadow. And since monomania of this sort is likely to lead in the end to the reiteration of one particular story, Charlie's invention began to

THE KERB IN THE SKY

grow thin and he eventually took to telling, over and over again, the first dream he had ever described – the story of his curious flight toward the moon in an aeroplane made of telephone wires. It was extremely painful. It saddened us all.

After a month or two, Charlie finally had to be sent to an asylum. I was out of town when they took him away, but Joe Fultz, who went with him, wrote me about it. 'He seemed to like it up here right away,' Joe wrote. 'He's calmer and his eyes look better.' (Charlie had developed a wild, hunted look.) 'Of course', concluded Joe, 'he's finally got away from that woman.'

It was a couple of weeks later that I drove up to the asylum to see Charlie. He was lying on a cot on a big screened-in porch, looking wan and thin. Dorothy was sitting on a chair beside his bed, bright-eyed and eager. I was somehow surprised to see her there, having figured that Charlie had, at least, won sanctuary from his wife. He looked quite mad. He began at once to tell me the story of his trip to the moon. He got to the part where the man who looked like Santa Claus waved at him to stop. 'He was in a plane made of telephone wires, too,' said Charlie. 'So I pulled over a kerb——'

'No. You pulled over to a *cloud*,' said Dorothy. 'There aren't any kerbs in the *sky*. There *couldn't* be. You pulled over to a cloud.'

Charlie sighed and turned slightly in his bed and looked at me. Dorothy looked at me, too, with her pretty smile.

'He always gets that story wrong,' she said.

The Civil War Phone-Number Association

Mr Rudy Vallée, in an interview (or maybe it was in an article), has said that sometimes when he goes backstage he is saddened at the sight of the members of his band sitting around reading detective stories. 'They should try to improve their memories,' says Mr Vallée, 'by associating telephone numbers, for instance, with the date of the Civil War.'

This remarkable statement can be picked to pieces by any skilful Civil War telephone-number associator. In the first place, the use of the phrase 'for instance' in the position we find it implies that Mr Vallée thinks it is a good idea to sit around associating *various* things with the date of the Civil War ('telephone numbers, for instance'). Such a practice would confound even Salo Finkelstein, the lightning calculator. If a person has put in the afternoon associating his bank balance, his automobile license plates, and the total amount of his debts with the date of the Civil War, he is

not going to be able to call up a phone number when he wants to; he is going to call up the money he has in the bank or the number on the back of his car. In the second place, it is futile to sit around, backstage or anywhere else, merely associating telephone numbers with the date of the Civil War and not calling anybody up. The purpose of the War of the Rebellion system of remembering phone numbers is not to keep them in the forefront of the mind, whence they can be brought up and recited to oneself as if they were limericks, but to tuck them away in the back of the mind, whence they can be called forth when needed and used for the practical purpose of getting in touch with somebody.

And in the third place, I must, as one of the oldest surviving veterans of the Civil War Telephone-Number Association, take firm exception to the expression 'the date of the Civil War'. The Civil War was full of dates, many of them – such as 19 September, the date of the Battle of Chickamauga – as important and helpful as the war years themselves. Mr Vallée's 'date' would seem to indicate that he goes simply by 1861, the year the war began, or 1865, the year it ended. These would be useful in fixing in one's mind only about half a dozen numbers, such as Bryant 9–1861, Wickersham 2–1865, maybe Watkins 9–1961 (if you remember to subtract a hundred years), and possibly Gramercy 7–5681. This last is, of course, 1865 backward and seems simple; but in a phone booth, without a pencil, one could call up practically everybody in the south-central part of town without getting the right party, unless one were very good at visualising four digits backward.

If I were Mr Vallée and knew only one date for the Civil War, I should certainly give up the whole system of association and write the numbers I wanted to remember in a small book and carry it about with me. Even I, who know dozens of Civil War dates, including the hour of day that Stonewall Jackson was shot, sometimes wish I had gone in for the 'jotting down' system. Using that method, if you get mad at somebody, you can cross out his number in the little notebook and be quit of it, whereas if you have it filed away in your mind alongside of Pickett's charge, it is there ineradicably. I still know the phone number of a girl who gave me the go-by in 1920, and now and then, as the years roll away, it flicks around the back of my head annoyingly, like a deer fly, upsetting my day. The phone number of the American Embassy in Paris, for which I no longer have any possible use, often keeps me awake at night: Passy 12.50. Particularly on trains: Passy douze cinquante, Passy douze cinquante, chant the iron wheels on the rails.

It was eight years ago that I began to go in for associating telephone numbers with troop movements, in a big way. At that time, which was before the fifth digit got into Manhattan phone numbers and made my life and Mr Vallée's even harder than they had been, my telephone number was Algonquin 9618. For some reason, that was hard for me. The Civil War fell down, in this case, almost completely, for although there was '61 in the middle to remember it by, the 9 and the 8 didn't seem to mean much. It was then that I began to toy with the other wars, the war with Spain naturally (and unfortunately) suggesting itself because of 98. As a result, I would phone 9861 and then 6198 and in the end go completely to pieces and try all the permutations until I had run the entire gamut of numbers in the Algonquin exchange, from 1689, the lowest, to 9861, the highest. For an old war associator to quit fiddling his life away in a phone booth and look up his number in the directory would be, of course, an unthinkable defeat that would leave its mark. The way I finally got Algonquin 9618 fixed in my mind, where it still stands as staunchly and as uselessly as an iron hitching post in a concrete walk, was to bring in the World War. I saw that by subtracting 4 from the last two digits – 18 – and adding it to the first two – 96 – I could make an even 100 of the first two. This made 14 out of the last two. I now had 10014 as a key number. This was useless unless I could plant in my memory some story, some war anecdote, which would break 10014 down into the proper arrangement of digits. The story I invented was this: that I had ended the war – that is, made '18 out of '14 – by sending overseas a male quartet from my company of 100 men (I figured myself as captain of a company with the full regulation Civil War strength of 100 men). This gave me, logically and smoothly, 9618.

My invention of the war anecdote was the beginning of an elaborate system of remembering telephone numbers in which sometimes as many as seven wars were involved, together with the movement of not only male quartets but bowling teams, football squads, rowing crews, and the like. For instance, to remember one number, I figured myself as an officer in the war with Mexico (a certain Lieutenant Chelsea) who sent a baseball nine to the aid of Napoleon at the Battle of Waterloo. The key number was 4615; the correct reading 3724. I simply sent my 9 from '46 to '15, you see.

The danger of this kind of preoccupation lies in the likelihood of confusing fact with fancy, shadow with substance, one's imaginary character with one's actual character. My reactions and reflexes in the workaday world began to be prompted now and then by the nature of my responsibilities as an officer in wars that ended long ago. I would sometimes, in the office, bark commands at my superiors. Things finally got so bad that for more than two years I never phoned anybody. In this way I managed to slough off from my overburdened subconscious something in the neighbourhood of a hundred and eighty numbers. Along with these vanished a lot of wearisome manoeuvres, such as the activities of a golfing foursome in the Seminole Indian War, and the extraordinary advent of three basketball teams at the Battle of Saratoga. Now I am back to a fairly normal basis, with the phone numbers of only about ninety-five people thundering in the indexes of my mind. Of these people, I am in actual contact with perhaps thirty. The others have moved away, or have broken up housekeeping, or have cut me off, or are dead. Their silly phone numbers, however, linger still, often in the night marching wearily along the border of a dream, on their way back from Moscow, General Pierre Gustave Toutant Beauregard riding ahead, the American Davis Cup team of 1919 bringing up the rear. Hooting and mocking, laughing and crying, they pass in review, all the old, lost numbers.

I wish I were a member of Rudy Vallée's band, peacefully reading a detective story.

Snapshot of a Dog

I ran across a dim photograph of him the other day, going through some old things. He's been dead twenty-five years. His name was Rex (my two brothers and I named him when we were in our early teens) and he was a bull terrier. 'An American bull terrier,' we used to say, proudly; none of your English bulls. He had one brindle eye that sometimes made him look like a clown and sometimes reminded you of a politician with a derby hat and cigar. The rest of him was white except for a brindle saddle that always seemed to be slipping off and a brindle stocking on a hind leg. Nevertheless, there was a nobility about him. He was big and muscular and beautifully made. He never lost his dignity even when trying to accomplish the extravagant tasks my brothers and myself used to set for him. One of these was the bringing of a ten-foot wooden rail into the yard through the back gate. We would throw it out into the alley and tell him to get it. Rex was as powerful as a wrestler, and there were not many things that he couldn't manage somehow to get hold of with his great jaws and lift or drag to wherever he wanted to put them, or wherever we wanted them put. He would catch the rail at the balance and lift it clear of the ground and trot with great confidence toward the gate. Of course, since the gate was only four feet wide or so, he couldn't bring the rail in broad-side. He found that out when he got a few terrific jolts, but he wouldn't give up. He finally figured out how to do it, by dragging the rail, holding on to one end, growling. He got a great, wagging satisfaction out of his work. We used to bet kids who had never seen Rex in action that he could catch a baseball thrown as high as they could throw it. He almost never let us down. Rex could hold a baseball with ease in his mouth, in one cheek, as if it were a chew of tobacco.

He was a tremendous fighter, but he never started fights. I don't believe he liked to get into them, despite the fact that he came from a line of fighters. He never went for another dog's throat but for one of its ears (that teaches a dog a lesson), and he would get his grip, close his eyes, and hold on. He could hold on for hours. His longest fight lasted from dusk until almost pitch-dark, one Sunday. It was fought in East Main Street in Columbus with a large, snarly nondescript that belonged to a big coloured man. When Rex finally got his ear grip, the brief whirlwind of snarling turned to screeching. It was frightening to listen to and to watch. The Negro boldly picked the dogs up somehow and began swinging them around his head, and finally let them fly like a hammer in a hammer throw, but although they landed ten feet away with a great plump, Rex still held on.

The two dogs eventually worked their way to the middle of the car tracks, and after a while two or three streetcars were held up by the fight. A motorman tried to pry Rex's jaws open with a switch rod; somebody lighted a fire and made a torch of a stick and held that to Rex's tail, but he paid no attention. In the end, all the residents and storekeepers in the neighbourhood were on hand, shouting this, suggesting that. Rex's joy of battle, when battle was joined, was almost tranquil. He had a kind of pleasant expression during fights, not a vicious one, his eyes closed in what would have seemed to be sleep had it not been for the turmoil of the struggle. The Oak Street Fire Department finally had to be sent for — I don't know why nobody thought of it sooner. Five or six pieces of apparatus arrived, followed by a battalion chief. A hose was attached and a powerful stream of water was turned on the dogs. Rex held on for several moments more while the torrent buffeted him about like a log in a freshet. He was a hundred yards away from where the fight started when he finally let go.

The story of the Homeric fight got all around town, and some of our relatives looked upon the incident as a blot on the family name. They insisted that we get rid of Rex, but we were very happy with him, and nobody could have made us give him up. We would have left town with him first, along any road there was to go. It would have been different, perhaps, if he had ever started fights, or looked for trouble. But he had a gentle disposition. He never bit a person in the ten strenuous years that he lived, nor ever growled at anyone except prowlers. He killed cats, that is true, but quickly and neatly and without especial malice, the way men kill certain animals. It was the only thing he did that we could never cure him of doing. He never killed, or even chased, a squirrel. I don't know why. He had his own philosophy about such things. He never ran barking after wagons or automobiles. He didn't seem to see the idea in pursuing something you couldn't catch, or something you couldn't do anything with, even if you did catch it. A wagon was one of the things he couldn't catch, or something you couldn't do anything with, even if you did catch it. A wagon was one of the things he couldn't tug along with his mighty jaws, and he knew it. Wagons therefore, were not a part of his world.

Swimming was his favourite recreation. The first time he ever saw a body of water (Alum Creek), he trotted nervously along the steep bank for a while, fell to barking wildly, and finally plunged in from a height of eight feet or more. I shall always remember that shining, virgin dive. Then he swam upstream and back just for the pleasure of it, like a man. It was fun to see him battle upstream against a stiff current, struggling and growling every foot of the way. He had as much fun in the water as any person I have known. You didn't have to throw a stick in the water to get him to go in. Of course, he would bring back a stick to you if you did throw one in. He would even have brought back a piano if you had thrown one in.

That reminds me of the night, way after midnight, when he went a-roving in the light of the moon and brought back a small chest of drawers that he found somewhere – how far from the house nobody ever knew; since it was Rex, it could easily have been half a mile. There were no drawers in the chest when he got it home, and it wasn't a good one – he hadn't taken it out of anybody's house; it was just an old cheap piece that somebody had abandoned on a trash heap. Still, it was something he wanted, probably because it presented a nice problem in transportation. It tested his mettle. We first knew about his achievement when, deep in the night, we heard him trying to get the chest up onto the porch. It sounded as if two or three people were trying to tear the house down. We came downstairs and turned on the porch light. Rex was on the top step trying to pull the thing up, but it had caught somehow and he was just holding his own. I suppose he would have held his own till dawn if we hadn't helped him. The next day we carted the chest miles away and threw it out. If we had thrown it out in a nearby alley, he would have brought it home again, as a small token of his integrity in such matters. After all, he had been taught to carry heavy wooden objects about, and he was proud of his prowess.

I am glad Rex never saw a trained police dog jump. He was just an amateur jumper himself, but the most daring and tenacious I have ever seen. He would take on any fence we pointed out to him. Six feet was easy for him, and he could do eight by making a tremendous leap and hauling himself over finally by his paws, grunting and straining; but he lived and died without knowing that twelve- and sixteen-foot walls were too much for him. Frequently, after letting him try to go over one for a while, we would have to carry him home. He would never have given up trying.

There was in his world no such thing as the impossible. Even death couldn't beat him down. He died, it is true, but only, as one of his admirers said, after 'straight-arming the death angel' for more than an hour. Late one afternoon he wandered home, too slowly and too uncertainly to be the Rex that had trotted briskly homeward up our avenue for ten years. I think we all knew when he came through the gate that he was dying. He had apparently taken a terrible beating, probably from the owner of some dog that he had got into a fight with. His head and body were scarred. His heavy collar with the teeth marks of many a battle on it was awry; some of the big brass studs in it were sprung loose from the leather. He licked at our hands and, staggering, fell, but got up again. We could see that he was looking for someone. One of his three masters was not home. He did not get home for an hour. During that hour the bull terrier fought against death as he had fought against the cold, strong current of Alum Creek, as he had fought to climb twelve-foot walls. When the person he was waiting for did come through the gate, whistling, ceasing to whistle, Rex walked a few wabbly paces toward him, touched his hand with his muzzle, and fell down again. This time he didn't get up.

Destructive Forces in Life

The mental efficiency books go into elaborate detail about how to attain Masterful Adjustment, as one of them calls it, but it seems to me that the problems they set up, and knock down, are in the main unimaginative and pedestrian: the little fusses at the breakfast-table, the routine troubles at the office, the familiar anxieties over money and health – the welter of workaday annoyances which all of us meet with and usually conquer without extravagant wear and tear. Let us examine, as a typical instance, a brief case history presented by the learned Mr David Seabury, author of *What Makes Us Seem So Queer, Unmasking Our Minds, Keep Your Wits, Growing Into Life,* and *How to Worry Successfully.* I select it at random. 'Frank Fulsome', writes Mr Seabury, 'flung down the book with disgust and growled an insult at his wife. That little lady put her hands to her face and fled from the room. She was sure Frank must hate her to speak so cruelly. Had she known it, he was not really speaking to her at all. The occasion merely gave vent to a pent-up desire to "punch his fool boss in the jaw".' This is, I believe, a characteristic Seabury situation. Many of the women in his treatises remind you of nobody so much as Ben Bolt's Alice, who 'wept with delight when you gave her a smile, and trembled with fear at your frown'. The little ladies most of us know would, instead of putting their hands to their faces and fleeing from the room, come right back at Frank Fulsome. Frank would perhaps be lucky if he didn't get a punch in the jaw himself. In any case, the situation would be cleared up in approximately three minutes. This 'had she known' business is not as common among wives to-day as Mr Seabury seems to think it is. The Latent Content (as the psychologists call it) of a husband's mind is usually as clear to the wife as the Manifest Content, frequently much clearer.

I could cite a dozen major handicaps to Masterful Adjustment which the thought technicians never touch upon, a dozen situation not so easy of analysis and solution as most of theirs. I will, however, content myself with one. Let us consider the case of a man of my acquaintance who had accomplished Discipline of Mind, overcome the Will to Fail, mastered the Technique of Living – had, in a word, practically attained Masterful Adjustment –

when he was called on the phone one afternoon about five o'clock by a man named Bert Scursey. The other man, whom I shall call Harry Conner, did not answer the phone, however; his wife answered it. As Scursey told me the story later, he had no intention when he dialled the Conners' apartment at the Hotel Graydon of doing more than talk with Harry. But, for some strange reason, when Louise Conner answered, Bert Scursey found himself pretending to be, and imitating the voice of, a coloured woman. This Scursey is by way of being an excellent mimic, and a coloured woman is one of the best things he does.

'Hello,' said Mrs Conner. In a plaintive voice, Scursey said, 'Is dis heah Miz Commah?' 'Yes, this is Mrs Conner,' said Louise. 'Who is speaking?' 'Dis heah's Edith Rummum,' said Scursey. 'Ah used wuck fo yo frens was nex doah yo place a Sou Norwuck.' Naturally, Mrs Conner did not follow this, and demanded rather sharply to know who was calling and what she wanted. Scursey, his voice soft with feigned tears, finally got it over to his friend's wife that he was one Edith Rummum, a coloured maid who had once worked for some friends of the Conners' in South Norwalk, where they had lived some years before. 'What is it you want, Edith?' asked Mrs Conner, who was completely taken in by the imposter (she could not catch the name of the South Norwalk friends, but let that go). Scursey – or Edith, rather – explained in a pitiable, hesitant way that she was without work or money and that she didn't know what she was going to do; Rummum, she said, was in the jailhouse because of a cutting scrape on a roller-coaster. Now, Louise Conner happened to be a most kind-hearted person, as Scursey well knew, so she said that she could perhaps find some laundry work for Edith to do. 'Yessum,' said Edith. 'Ah laundas.' At this point, Harry Conner's voice, raised in the room behind his wife, came clearly to Scursey, saying, 'Now, for God's sake, Louise, don't go giving our clothes out to somebody you never saw or heard of in your life.' This interjection of Conner's was in firm keeping with a theory of logical behaviour which he had got out of the Mind and Personality books. There was no Will to Weakness here, no Desire to Have His Shirts Ruined, no False Sympathy for the Coloured Woman Who Has Not Organised Her Life.

But Mrs Conner who often did not listen to Mr Conner, in spite of his superior mental discipline, prevailed.* 'Where are you now,

* This sometimes happens even when the husband is mentally disciplined and the wife is not

*A mentally disciplined husband and
a mentally undisciplined wife*

Edith?' she asked. This disconcerted Scursey for a moment, but he
finally said, 'Ah's jes rounda corna, Miz Commah.' 'Well, you
come over to the Hotel Graydon,' said Mrs Conner. 'We're in
Apartment 7-A on the seventh floor.' 'Yessm,' said Edith. Mrs
Conner hung up and so did Scursey. He was now, he realised, in
something of predicament. Since he did not possess a streamlined
mind, as Dr Mursell has called it, and definitely a Will to Confuse,
he did not perceive that his little joke had gone far enough. He
wanted to go on with it, which is a characteristic of woolgatherers,
pranksters, wags, wish-fulfillers, and escapists generally. He
enjoyed fantasy as much as reality, probably even more, which is
a sure symptom of Regression, Digression, and Analogical Redin-
tegration. What he finally did, therefore, was to call back the
Conners and get Mrs Conner on the phone again. 'Jeez, Miss
Commah,' he said, with a hint of panic in his voice, 'Ah cain' fine
yo appottoman!' 'Where are you, Edith?' she asked. 'Lawd, Ah
doan know,' said Edith. 'Ah's on *some* floah in de Hotel Graydon.'
'Well, listen, Edith, you took the elevator, didn't you?' 'Das whut
Ah took,' said Edith uncertainly. 'Well, you go back to the elevator
and tell the boy you want to get off at the seventh floor. I'll meet
you at the elevator.' 'Yessm,' said Edith, with even more uncertainty. At this point, Conner's loud voice, speaking to his wife, was
again heard by Scursey. 'Where in the hell is she calling from?'
demanded Conner, who had developed Logical Reasoning. 'She
must have wandered into somebody else's apartment if she is
calling you from this building, for God's sake!' Whereupon, having no desire to explain where Edith was calling from, Scursey
hung up.

After an instant of thought, or rather Disintegrated Phantas-magoria, Scursey rang the Conners again. He wanted to prevent Louise from going out to the elevator and checking up with the operator. This time, as Scursey had hoped, Harry Conner ans-wered, having told his wife that he would handle this situation. 'Hello!' shouted Conner, irritably. 'Who is this?' Scursey now abandoned the role of Edith and assumed a sharp, fussy, mas-culine tone. 'Mr Conner,' he said, crisply, 'this is the office. I am afraid we shall have to ask you to remove this coloured person from the building. She is blundering into other people's apart-ments, using their phones. We cannot have that sort of thing, you know, at the Graydon.' The man's words and his tone infuriated Conner. 'There are a lot of sort of things I'd like to see you not have at the Graydon!' he shouted. 'Well, please come down to the lobby and do something about this situation,' said the man, nas-tily. 'You're damned right I'll come down!' howled Conner. He banged down the receiver.

Bert Scursey sat in a chair and gloated over the involved state of affairs which he had created. He decided to go over to the Graydon, which was just up the street from his own apartment, and see what was happening. It promised to have all the confusion which his disorderly mind so deplorably enjoyed. And it did have. He found Conner in a tremendous rage in the lobby, accusing an astonished assistant manager of having insulted him. Several per-sons in the lobby watched the curious scene. 'But, Mr Conner,' said the assistant manager, a Mr Bent, 'I have no idea what you are talking about.' 'If you listen, you'll find out!' bawled Harry Con-ner. 'In the first place, the coloured woman's coming to the hotel was no idea of mine. I've never seen her in my life and I don't want to see her! I want to go to my *grave* without seeing her!' He had forgotten what the Mind and Personality books had taught him; never raise your voice in anger, always stick to the point. Natur-ally, Mr Bent could only believe that his guest had gone out of his mind. He decided to humour him. 'Where is this – ah – coloured woman, Mr Conner?' he asked, warily. He was somewhat pale and was fiddling with a bit of paper. A dabbler in psychology books himself, he knew that coloured women are often Sex Degradation symbols, and he wondered if Conner had not fallen out of love with his wife without realising it. (This theory, I believe, Mr Bent has clung to ever since, although the Conners are one of the happiest couples in the country.) 'I don't know where she is!' cried Conner. 'She's up on some other floor phoning my wife! You seemed to know all about it! I had nothing to do with it! I opposed it from the start! But I want no insults from you no matter *who* opposed it!' 'Certainly not, certainly not,' said Mr Bent, backing slightly away. He began to wonder what he was going to do with this maniac.

At this juncture Scursey, who had been enjoying the scene at a safe distance, approached Conner and took him by the arm. 'What's the matter, old boy?' he asked. 'H'lo, Bert,' said Conner, sullenly.And then, his eyes narrowing, he began to examine the look on Scursey's face. Scursey is not good at deadpanning; he is only good on the phone. There was a guilty grin on his face. 'You—' said Conner, bitterly, remembering Scursey's pranks of mimicry, and he turned on his heel, walked to the elevator, and, when Scursey tried to get in too, shoved him back into the lobby. That was the end of the friendship between the Conners and Bert Scursey. It was more than that. It was the end of Harry Conner's stay at the Graydon. It was, in fact the end of his stay in New York City. He and Louise live in Oregon now, where Conner accepted a less important position than he had held in New York because the episode of Edith had turned him against Scursey, Mr Bent, the Graydon, and the whole metropolitan area.

Anybody can handle the Frank Fulsomes of the world, but is there anything to be done about the Bert Scurseys? Can we so streamline our minds that the antics of the Scurseys roll off them like water off a duck's back? I don't think so. I believe the authors of the inspirational books don't think so, either, but are afraid to attack the subject. I imagine they have been hoping nobody would bring it up. Hardly anybody goes through life without encountering his Bert Scursey and having his life – and his mind – accordingly modified. I have known a dozen Bert Scurseys. I have often wondered what happened to some of their victims. There was, for example, the man who rang up a waggish friend of mine by mistake, having got a wrong number. 'Is this the Shu-Rite Shoestore?' the caller asked, querulously. 'Shu-Rite Shoestore, good morning!' said my friend, brightly. 'Well,' said the other, 'I just called up to say that the shoes I bought there a week ago are shoddy. They're made, by God, of cardboard. I'm going to bring them in and show you. I want satisfaction!' 'And you shall have it!' said my friend. 'Our shoes are, as you say, shoddy. There have been many complaints, many complaints . Our shoes, I am afraid, simply go to pieces on the foot. We shall, of course, refund your money.' I know another man who was always being roused out of bed by people calling a certain railway which had a similar phone number. 'When can I get a train to Buffalo?' a sour-voiced woman demanded one morning about seven o'clock. 'Not till 2 a.m. to-morrow, madam,' said this man. 'But that's ridiculous!' cried the woman. 'I know,' said the man, 'and we realise that. Hence we include, in the regular fare, a taxi which will call for you in plenty of time to make the train. Where do you live?' The lady, slightly mollified, told him an address in the Sixties. 'We'll have a cab there at one-thirty, madam,' he said. 'The driver will handle your baggage.' 'Now I can count on that?' she said. 'Certainly, madam,' he told her. 'One-thirty, sharp.'

Just what changes were brought about in that woman's character by that call, I don't know. But the thing might have altered the colour and direction of her life, the pattern of her mind, the whole fabric of her nature. Thus we see that a person might build up a streamlined mind, a mind awakened to a new life, a new discipline, only to have the whole works shot to pieces by so minor and unpredictable a thing as a wrong telephone number. On the other hand, the undisciplined mind would never have the fortitude to consider a trip to Buffalo at two in the morning, nor would it have the determination to seek redress from a shoe-store which had sold it a faulty pair of shoes. Hence the undisciplined mind runs far less chance of having its purposes thwarted, its plans distorted, its whole scheme and system wrenched out of line. The undisciplined mind, in short, is far better adapted to the confused world in which we live to-day than the streamlined mind. This is, I am afraid, no place for the streamlined mind.

Nine Needles

One of the more spectacular minor happenings of the past few years which I am sorry that I missed took place in the Columbus, Ohio, home of some friends of a friend of mine. It seems that a Mr Albatross, while looking for something in his medicine cabinet one morning, discovered a bottle of a kind of patent medicine which his wife had been taking for a stomach ailment. Now, Mr Albatross is one of those apprehensive men who are afraid of patent medicines and of almost everything else. Some weeks before, he had encountered a paragraph in a Consumers' Research bulletin which announced that this particular medicine was bad for you. He had thereupon ordered his wife to throw out what was left of her supply of the stuff and never buy any more. She had promised, and here now was another bottle of the perilous liquid. Mr Albatross, a man given to quick rages, shouted the conclusion of the story at my friend: 'I threw the bottle out of the bathroom window and the medicine chest after it!' It seems to me that must have been a spectacle worth going a long way to see.

I am sure that many a husband has wanted to wrench the family medicine cabinet off the wall and throw it out of the window, if only because the average medicine cabinet is so filled with mysterious bottles and unidentifiable objects of all kinds that it is a source of constant bewilderment and exasperation to the American male. Surely the British medicine cabinet and the French medicine cabinet and all the other medicine cabinets must be simpler and better ordered than ours. It may be that the American habit of saving everything and never throwing anything away, even empty bottles, causes the domestic medicine cabinet to become as cluttered in its small way as the American attic becomes cluttered in its major way. I have encountered few medicine cabinets in this country which were not pack-jammed with something between a hundred and fifty and two hundred different items, from dental floss to boracic acid, from razor blades to sodium perborate, from adhesive tape to coconut oil. Even the neatest wife will put off clearing out the medicine cabinet on the ground that she has something else to do that is more important at the moment, or more diverting. It was in the apartment of such a wife and her husband that I became enormously involved with a medicine cabinet one morning not long ago.

I had spent the week-end with this couple – they live on East Tenth Street near Fifth Avenue – such a week-end as left me reluctant to rise up on Monday morning with bright and shining face and go to work. They got up and went to work, but I didn't. I didn't get up until about two-thirty in the afternoon. I had my face all lathered for shaving and the washbowl was full of hot water when suddenly I cut myself with the razor. I cut my ear. Very few men cut their ears with razors, but I do, possibly because I was taught the old Spencerian free-wrist movement by my writing teacher in the grammar grades. The ear bleeds rather profusely when cut with a razor and is difficult to get at. More angry than hurt, I jerked open the door of the medicine cabinet to see if I could find a styptic pencil and out fell, from the top shelf, a little black paper packet containing nine needles. It seems that this wife kept a little paper packet containing nine needles on the top shelf of the medicine cabinet. The packet fell into the soapy water of the wash-bowl, where the paper rapidly disintegrated, leaving nine needles at large in the bowl. I was, naturally enough, not in the best condition, either physical or mental, to recover nine needles from a wash-bowl. No gentleman who has lather on his face and whose ear is bleeding is in the best condition for anything, even something involving the handling of nine large blunt objects.

It did not seem wise to me to pull the plug out of the wash-bowl and let the needles go down the drain. I had visions of clogging up the plumbing system of the house, and also a vague fear of causing short circuits somehow or other (I know very little about electricity and I don't want to have it explained to me). Finally, I groped very gently around the bowl and eventually had four of the needles in the palm of one hand and three in the palm of the other – two I couldn't find. If I thought quickly and clearly, I wouldn't have done that. A lathered man whose ear is bleeding and who has four wet needles in one hand and three in the other may be said to have reached the lowest known point of human efficiency. There is nothing he can do but stand there. I tried transferring the needles in my left hand to the palm of my right hand, but I couldn't get them off my left hand. Wet needles cling to you. In the end, I wiped the needles off onto a bath-towel which was hanging on a rod above the bath-tub. It was the only towel that I could find. I had to dry my hands afterwards on the bath-mat. Then I tried to find the needles in the towel. Hunting for seven needles in a

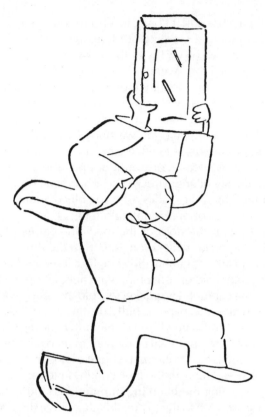

And the medicine chest after it!

bath-towel is the most tedious occupation I have ever engaged in. I could find only five of them. With the two that had been left in the bowl, that meant there were four needles in all missing – two in the wash-bowl and two others lurking in the towel or lying in the bath-tub under the towel. Frightful thoughts came to me of what might happen to anyone who used that towel or washed his face in the bowl or got into the tub, if I didn't find the missing needles. Well, I didn't find them. I sat down on the edge of the tub to think, and I decided finally that the only thing to do was wrap up the towel in a newspaper and take it away with me. I also decided to leave a note for my friends explaining as clearly as I could that I was afraid there were two needles in the bath-tub and two needles in the wash-bowl, and that they better be careful.

I looked everywhere in the apartment, but I could not find a pencil, or a pen, or a typewriter. I could find pieces of paper, but nothing with which to write on them. I don't know what gave me the idea – a movie I had seen, perhaps, or a story I had read – but I suddenly thought of writing a message with a lipstick. The wife might have an extra lipstick lying around and, if so, I concluded it would be in the medicine cabinet. I went back to the medicine cabinet and began poking around in it for a lipstick. I saw what I thought looked like the metal tip of one, and I got two fingers around it and began to pull gently – it was under a lot of things. Every object in the medicine cabinet began to slide. Bottles broke in the wash-bowl and on the floor; red, brown, and white liquids spurted; nail files, scissors, razor blades, and miscellaneous objects sang and clattered and tinkled. I was covered with perfume, peroxide, and cold cream.

It took me half an hour to get the debris all together in the middle of the bathroom floor. I made no attempt to put anything back in the medicine cabinet. I knew it would take a steadier hand than mine and a less shattered spirit. Before I went away (only partly shaved) and abandoned the shambles, I left a note saying that I was afraid there were needles in the bath-tub and the wash-bowl and that I had taken their towel and that I would call up and tell them everything – I wrote it in iodine with the end of a toothbrush. I have not yet called up, I am sorry to say. I have neither found the courage nor thought up the words to explain what happened. I suppose my friends believe that I deliberately smashed up their bathroom and stole their towel. I don't know for sure, because they have not yet called me up, either.

Doc Marlowe

I was too young to be other than awed and puzzled by Doc Marlowe when I knew him. I was only sixteen when he died. He was sixty-seven. There was that vast difference in our ages and there was a vaster difference in our backgrounds. Doc Marlowe was a medicine-show man. He had been a lot of other things, too: a circus man, the proprietor of a concession at Coney Island, a saloon-keeper; but in his fifties he had travelled around with a tent-show troupe made up of a Mexican named Chickalilli, who threw knives, and a man called Professor Jones, who played the banjo. Doc Marlowe would come out after the entertainment and harangue the crowd and sell bottles of medicine for all kinds of ailments. I found out all this about him gradually, towards the last, and after he died. When I first knew him, he represented the Wild West to me, and there was nobody I admired so much.

I met Doc Marlowe at old Mrs Willoughby's rooming-house. She had been a nurse in our family, and I used to go and visit her over week-ends sometimes, for I was very fond of her. I was about eleven years old then. Doc Marlowe wore scarred leather leggings, a bright-coloured bead vest that he said he got from the Indians, and a ten-gallon hat with kitchen matches stuck in the band, all the way around. He was about six feet four inches tall, with big shoulders, and a long, drooping moustache. He let his hair grow long, like General Custer's. He had a wonderful collection of Indian relics and six-shooters, and he used to tell me stories of his adventures in the Far West. His favourite expressions were 'Hay, boy!' and 'Hay, boy-gie!' which he used the way some people now use 'Hot dog!' or 'Doggone!' He told me once that he had killed an Indian chief named Yellow Hand in a tomahawk duel on horseback. I though he was the greatest man I had ever seen. It wasn't until he died and his son came on from New Jersey for the funeral that I found out he had never been in the Far West in his life. He had been born in Brooklyn.

Doc Marlowe had given up the road when I knew him, but he still dealt in what he called 'medicines'. His stock in trade was a liniment that he had called Snake Oil when he travelled around.

He changed the name to Blackhawk Liniment when he settled in Columbus. Doc didn't always sell enough of it to pay for his bed and board, and old Mrs Willoughby would sometimes have to 'trust' him for weeks at a time. She didn't mind, because his liniment had taken a bad kink out of her right limb that had bothered her for thirty years. I used to see people whom Doc had massaged with Blackhawk Liniment move arms and legs that they hadn't been able to move before he 'treated' them. His patients were day labourers, wives of tramcar conductors and people like that. Sometimes they would shout and weep after Doc had massaged them and several got up and walked around who hadn't been able to walk before. One man hadn't turned his head to either side for seven years before Doc soused him with Blackhawk. In half an hour he could move his head as easily as I could move mine. 'Glory be to God!' he shouted. 'It's the secret qualities

A man called Professor Jones

in the ointment my friend,' Doc Marlowe told him, suavely. He always called the liniment ointment.

News of his miracles got around by word of mouth among the poorer classes to town – he was not able to reach the better people (the 'tony folks', he called them) – but there was never a big enough sale to give Doc a steady income. For one thing, people thought there was more magic in Doc's touch than in his liniment, and, for another, the ingredients of Blackhawk cost so much that his profits were not very great. I know, because I used to go to the wholesale chemical company once in a while for him and buy his supplies. Everything that went into the liniment was standard and expensive (and well known, not secret). A man at the company told me he didn't see how Doc could make much money on it at thirty-five cents a bottle. But even when he was very low in funds Doc never cut out any of the ingredients or substituted cheaper ones. Mrs Willoughby had suggested it to him once, she told me, when she was helping him 'put up a batch', and he had got mad. 'He puts a heap of store by that liniment being right up to the mark,' she said.

Doc added to his small earnings, I discovered, by money he made gambling. He used to win quite a few dollars on Saturday nights at Freck's saloon, playing poker with the marketmen and the railwaymen who dropped in there. It wasn't for several years that I found out Doc cheated. I had never heard about marked cards until he told me about them and showed me his. It was one rainy afternoon, after he had played seven-up with Mrs Willoughby and old Mr Peiffer, another roomer of hers. They had played for small stakes (Doc wouldn't play cards unless there was some money up, and Mrs Willoughby wouldn't play if very much was up). Only twenty or thirty cents had changed hands in the end. Doc had won it all. I remember my astonishment and indignation when it dawned on me that Doc had used the marked cards in playing the old lady and the old man. 'You didn't cheat *them*, did you?' I asked him. 'Jimmy, my boy,' he told me, 'the man that calls the turn wins the money.' His eyes twinkled and he seemed to enjoy my anger. I was outraged, but I was helpless. I knew I could never tell Mrs Willoughby about how Doc had cheated her at seven-up. I liked her, but I liked him, too. Once he had given me a whole dollar to buy fireworks with on the Fourth of July.

I remember once, when I was staying at Mrs Willoughby's, Doc Marlowe was roused out of bed in the middle of the night by a poor woman who was frantic because her little girl was sick. This

woman had had the sciatica driven out of her by his liniment, she
reminded Doc. He placed her then. She had never been able to
pay him a cent for his liniment or his 'treatments', and he had
given her a great many. He got up and dressed, and went over to
her house. The child had colic, I suppose. Doc couldn't have had
any idea what was the matter, but he sopped on liniment; he
sopped on a whole bottle. When he came back home, two hours
later, he said he had 'relieved the distress'. The little girl had gone
to sleep and was all right the next day, whether on account of Doc
Marlowe or in spite of him I don't know. 'I want to thank you,
doctor,' said the mother, tremulously, when she called on him that
afternoon. He gave her another bottle of liniment, and he didn't
charge her for it or for his 'professional call'. He used to massage,
and give liniment to, a lot of sufferers who were too poor to pay.
Mrs Willoughby told him once that he was too generous and too
easily taken in. Doc laughed – and winked at me, with the twinkle
in his eye that he had had when he told me how he had cheated
the old lady at cards.

Once I went for a walk with him out Town Street on a Saturday
afternoon. It was a warm day, and after a while I said I wanted a
soda. Well, he said, he didn't care if he took something himself.
We went into a drugstore, and I ordered a chocolate soda and he
had a lemon phosphate. When we had finished, he said, 'Jimmy,
my son, I'll match you to see who pays for the drinks.' He handed
me a quarter and he told me to toss the quarter and he would call
the turn. He called heads and won. I paid for the drinks. It left me
with a dime.

I was fifteen when Doc got out his pamphlets, as he called them.
He had eased the misery of the wife of a small-time printer and the
grateful man had given him a special price on two thousand
advertising pamphlets. There was very little in them about Blackhawk Liniment. They were mostly about Doc himself and his *Life
in the Far West*. He had gone out to Franklin Park one day with a
photographer – another of his numerous friends – and there the
photographer took dozens of pictures of Doc, a lariat in one hand,
a six-shooter in the other. I had gone along. When the pamphlets
came out, there were the pictures of Doc, peering around trees,
crouching behind bushes, whirling the lariat, aiming the gun. 'Dr
H. H. Marlowe Hunting Indians' was one of the captions. 'Dr H.
M. Marlowe after Hoss-Thieves' was another one. He was very
proud of the pamphlets and always had a sheaf with him. He
would pass them out to people on the street.

Two years before he died Doc got hold of an ancient wheezy Cadillac somewhere. He aimed to start travelling around again, he said, but he never did, because the old automobile was so worn out it wouldn't hold up for more than a mile or so. It was about this time that a man named Hardman and his wife came to stay at Mrs Willoughby's. They were farm people from around Lancaster who had sold their place. They got to like Doc because he was so jolly, they said, and they enjoyed his stories. He treated Mrs Hardman for an old complaint in the small of her back and wouldn't take any money for it. They thought he was a fine gentleman. Then there came a day when they announced that they were going to St. Louis, where they had a son. They talked some of settling in St. Louis. Doc Marlowe told them they ought to buy a nice auto cheap and drive out, instead of going by train – it wouldn't cost much and they could see the country, give themselves a treat. Now, he knew where they could pick up just such a car.

Of course, he finally sold them the decrepit Cadillac – it had been stored away somewhere in the back of a garage whose owner kept it there for nothing because Doc had relieved his mother of a distress in the groins, as Doc explained it. I don't know just how the garage man doctored up the car, but he did. It actually chugged along pretty steadily when Doc took the Hardmans out for a trial spin. He told them he hated to part with it, but he finally let them have it for a hundred dollars. I knew, of course, and so did Doc, that couldn't last many miles.

Doc got a letter from the Hardmans in St. Louis, ten days later. They had had to abandon the old junk pile in West Jefferson, some fifteen miles out of Columbus. Doc read the letter aloud to me, peering over his glasses, his eyes twinkling, every now and then punctuating the lines with 'Hay boy!' and 'Hay, Boy-gie!' 'I just want you to know, Dr Marlowe,' he read, 'what I think of low-life swindlers like you [Hay, boy!] and that it will be a long day before I put my trust in a two-faced lyer and imposture again [Hay, boy-gie!]. The garrage man in W. Jefferson told us your old rattle-trap had been doctored up just to fool us. It was a low-down dirty trick as no swine would play on a white man [Hay, boy!].' Far from being disturbed by the letter, Doc Marlowe was plainly amused. He took off his glasses, after he had finished it and laughed, his hand to his brow and his eyes closed. I was pretty mad, because I liked the Hardmans, and because they had liked him. Doc Marlowe put the letter carefully back into its envelope and tucked it away in his inside pocket, as if it were something precious. Then he picked up a pack of cards and began to lay out a solitaire hand. 'want to set in a little seven-up game, Jimmy?' he asked me. I was furious. 'Not with a cheater like you!' I shouted, and stamped out of the room, slamming the door. I could hear him chuckling to himself behind me.

The last time I saw Doc Marlowe was just a few days before he died. I didn't know anything about death, but I knew that he was dying when I saw him. His voice was very faint and his face was drawn; they told me he had a lot of pain. When I got ready to leave the room he asked me to bring him a tin box that was on his bureau. I got it and handed it to him. He poked around in it for awhile with unsteady fingers and finally found what he wanted. He handed it to me. It was a quarter, or rather it looked like a quarter, but it had heads on both sides. 'Never let the other fella call the turn, Jimmy, my boy,' said Doc, with a shadow of his old twinkle and the echo of his old chuckle. I still have the two-headed quarter. For a long time I didn't like to think about it, or about Doc Marlowe, but I do now.

The Little Girl and the Wolf

One afternoon a big wolf waited in a dark forest for a little girl to come along carrying a basket of food to her grandmother. Finally a little girl did come along and she was carrying a basket of food. 'Are you carrying that basket to your grandmother?' asked the wolf. The little girl said yes, she was. So the wolf asked her where her grandmother lived and the little girl told him and he disappeared into the wood.

When the little girl opened the door of her grandmother's house she saw that there was somebody in bed with a nightcap and nightgown on. She had approached no nearer than twenty-five feet from the bed when she saw that it was not her grandmother but the wolf, for even in a nightcap a wolf does not look any more like your grandmother than the Metro-Goldwyn lion looks like Calvin Coolidge. So the little girl took an automatic out of her basket and shot the wolf dead.

Moral: It is not so easy to fool little girls nowadays as it used to be.

The Scotty Who Knew Too Much

Several summers ago there was a Scotty who went to the country for a visit. He decided that all the farm dogs were cowards, because they were afraid of a certain animal that had a white stripe down its back. 'You are a pussy-cat and I can lick you,' the Scotty said to the farm dog who lived in the house where the Scotty was visiting. 'I can lick the little animal with the white stripe, too. Show him to me.' 'Don't you want to ask any questions about him?' said the farm dog. 'Naw,' said the Scotty. '*You* ask the questions.'

So the farm dog took the Scotty into the woods and showed him the white-striped animal and the Scotty closed in on him, growling and slashing. It was all over in a moment and the Scotty lay on his back. When he came to, the farm dog said, 'What happened?' 'He threw vitriol,' said the Scotty, 'but he never laid a glove on me.'

A few days later the farm dog told the Scotty there was another animal all the farm dogs were afraid of. 'Lead me to him,' said the Scotty. 'I can lick anything that doesn't wear horseshoes.' 'Don't you want to ask any questions about him?' said the farm dog. 'Naw,' said the Scotty. 'Just show me where he hangs out.' So the farm dog led him to a place in the woods and pointed out the little animal when he came along. 'A clown,' said the Scotty, 'a pushover,' and he closed in, leading with his left and exhibiting some mighty fancy footwork. In less than a second the Scotty was flat on his back, and when he woke up the farm dog was pulling quills out of him. 'What happened?' said the farm dog. 'He pulled a knife on me,' said the Scotty, 'but at least I have learned how you fight out here in the country, and now I am going to beat *you* up.' So he closed in on the farm dog, holding his nose with one front paw to ward of the vitriol and covering his eyes with the other front paw to keep out the knives. The Scotty couldn't see his opponent and he couldn't smell his opponent and he was so badly beaten that he had to be taken back to the city and put in a nursing home.

Moral: It is better to ask some of the questions than to know all the answers.

The Bear Who Let It Alone

In the woods of the Far West there once lived a brown bear who could take it or let it alone. He would go into a bar where they sold mead, a fermented drink made of honey, and he would have just two drinks. Then he would put some money on the bar and say, 'See what the bears in the back room will have,' and he would go home. But finally he took to drinking by himself most of the day. He would reel home at night, kick over the umbrella stand, knock down the bridge lamps, and ram his elbows through the windows. Then he would collapse on the floor and lie there until he went to sleep. His wife was greatly distressed and his children were very frightened.

At length the bear saw the error of his ways and began to reform. In the end he became a famous teetotaller and a persistent temperance lecturer. He would tell everybody that came to his house about the awful effects of drink, and he would boast about how strong and well he had become since he gave up touching the stuff. To demonstrate this, he would stand on his head and on his hands and he would turn cartwheels in the house, kicking over the umbrella stand, knocking down the bridge lamps, and ramming his elbows through the windows. Then he would lie down on the floor, tired by his healthful exercise, and go to sleep. His wife was greatly distressed and his children were very frightened.

Moral: You might as well fall flat on your face as lean over too far backward.

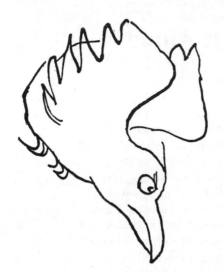

The Shrike and the Chipmunks

Once upon a time there were two chipmunks, a male and a female. The male chipmunk thought that arranging nuts in artistic patterns was more fun than just piling them up to see how many you could pile up. The female was all for piling up as many as you could. She told her husband that if he gave up making designs with the nuts there would be room in their large cave for a great many more and he would soon become the wealthiest chipmunk in the woods. But he would not let her interfere with his designs, so she flew into a rage and left him. 'The shrike will get you,' she said, 'because you are helpless and cannot look after yourself.' To be sure, the female chipmunk had not been gone three nights before the male had to dress for a banquet and could not find his studs or shirt or suspenders. So he couldn't go to the banquet, but that was just as well, because all the chipmunks who did go were attacked and killed by a weasel.

The next day the shrike began hanging around outside the chipmunk's cave, waiting to catch him. The shrike couldn't get in because the doorway was clogged up with soiled laundry and dirty dishes. 'He will come out for a walk after breakfast and I will get him then,' thought the shrike. But the chipmunk slept all day and did not get up and have breakfast until after dark. Then he came out for a breath of air before beginning work on a new design. The shrike swooped down to snatch up the chipmunk, but could not see very well on account of the dark, so he batted his head against an alder branch and was killed.

A few days later the female chipmunk returned and saw the awful mess the house was in. She went to the bed and shook her husband. 'What would you do without me?' she demanded. 'Just go on living, I guess,' he said. 'You wouldn't last five days,' she told him. She swept the house and did the dishes and sent out the laundry, and then she made the chipmunk get up and wash and dress. 'You can't be healthy if you lie in bed all day and never get any exercise,' she told him. So she took him for a walk in the bright sunlight and they were both caught and killed by the shrike's brother, a shrike named Stoop.

Moral: Early to rise and early to bed makes a male healthy and wealthy and dead.

The Crow and the Oriole

Once upon a time a crow fell in love with a Baltimore oriole. He had seen her flying past his nest every spring on her way North and every autumn on her way South, and he had decided that she was a tasty dish. He had observed that she came North every year with a different gentleman, but he paid no attention to the fact that all the gentlemen were Baltimore orioles. 'Anybody can have that mouse,' he said to himself. So he went to his wife and told her that he was in love with a Baltimore oriole who was as cute as a cuff link. He said he wanted a divorce, so his wife gave him one simply by opening the door and handing him his hat. 'Don't come crying to me when she throws you down,' she said. 'That fly-by-season hasn't got a brain in her head. She can't cook or sew. Her upper register sounds like a streetcar taking a curve. You can find out in any dictionary that the crow is the smartest and most capable of birds – or was till you became one.' 'Tush!' said the male crow. 'Pish! You are simply a jealous woman.' He tossed her a few dollars. 'Here,' he said, 'go buy yourself some finery. You look like the bottom of an old teakettle.' And off he went to look for the oriole.

This was in the springtime and he met her coming North with an oriole he had never seen before. The crow stopped the female oriole and pleaded his cause – or should we say cawed his pleas? At any rate, he courted her in a harsh, grating voice, which made her laugh merrily. 'You sound like an old window shutter,' she said, and she snapped her fingers at him. 'I am bigger and stronger than your gentleman friend,' said the crow. 'I have a vocabulary larger than his. All the orioles in the country couldn't even lift the corn I own. I am a fine sentinel and my voice can be heard for miles in case of danger.' 'I don't see how that could interest anybody but another crow,' said the female oriole, and she laughed at him and flew on toward the North. The male oriole tossed the crow some coins. 'Here,' he said, 'go buy yourself a blazer or something. You look like the bottom of an old coffeepot.'

The crow flew back sadly to his nest, but his wife was not there.

He found a note pinned to the front door. 'I have gone away with Bert,' it read. 'You will find some arsenic in the medicine chest.'

Moral: Even the llama should stick to mamma.

The Glass in the Field

A short time ago some builders, working on a studio in Connecticut, left a huge square of plate glass standing upright in a field one day. A goldfinch flying swiftly across the field struck the glass and was knocked cold. When he came to he hastened to his club, where an attendant bandaged his head and gave him a stiff drink. 'What the hell happened?' asked a sea gull. 'I was flying across a meadow when all of a sudden the air cystallised on me,' said the goldfinch. The sea gull and a hawk and an eagle all laughed heartily. A swallow listened gravely. 'For fifteen years, fledgling and bird, I've flown this country,' said the eagle, 'and I assure you there is no such thing as air crystallising. Water, yes; air, no.' 'You were probably struck by a hailstone,' the hawk told the goldfinch. 'Or he may have had a stroke,' said the sea gull. 'What do you think, swallow?' 'Why, I—I think maybe the air crystallised on him,' said the swallow. The large birds laughed so loudly that the goldfinch became annoyed and bet them each a dozen worms that they couldn't follow the course he had flown across the field without encountering the hardened atmosphere. They all took his bet; the swallow went along to watch. The sea gull, the eagle, and the hawk decided to fly together over the route the goldfinch indicated. 'You come, too,' they said to the swallow. 'I—I—well, no,' said the swallow. 'I don't think I will.' So the three large birds took off together and they hit the glass together and they were all knocked cold.

Moral: He who hesitates is sometimes saved.

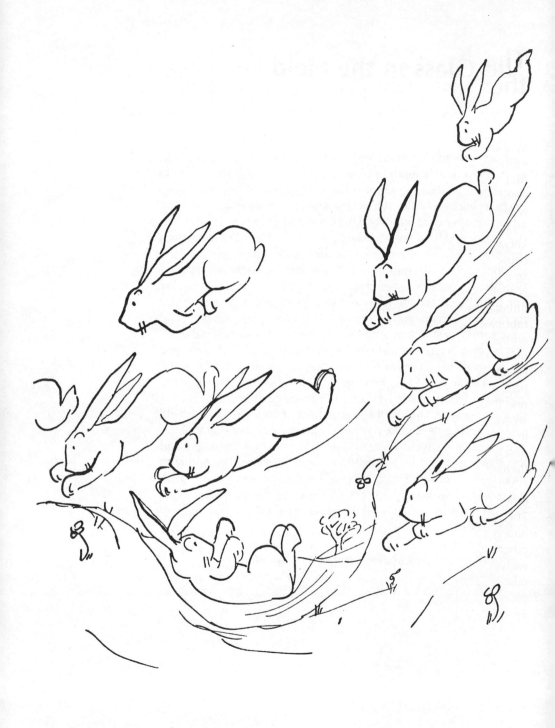

The Rabbits Who Caused All the Trouble

Within the memory of the youngest child there was a family of rabbits who lived near a pack of wolves. The wolves announced that they did not like the way the rabbits were living. (The wolves were crazy about the way they themselves were living, because it was the only way to live.) One night several wolves were killed in an earthquake and this was blamed on the rabbits, for it is well known that rabbits pound on the ground with their hind legs and cause earthquakes. On another night one of the wolves was killed by a bolt of lightning and this was also blamed on the rabbits, for it is well known that lettuce-eaters cause lightning. The wolves threatened to civilise the rabbits if they didn't behave, and the rabbits decided to run away to a desert island. But the other animals, who lived at a great distance, shamed them, saying, 'You must stay where you are and be brave. This is no world for escapists. If the wolves attack you, we will come to your aid, in all probability.' So the rabbits continued to live near the wolves and one day there was a terrible flood which drowned a great many wolves. This was blamed on the rabbits, for it is well known that carrot-nibblers with long ears cause floods. The wolves descended on the rabbits, for their own good, and imprisoned them in a dark cave, for their own protection.

When nothing was heard about the rabbits for some weeks, the other animals demanded to know what had happened to them. The wolves replied that the rabbits had been eaten and since they had been eaten the affair was a purely internal matter. But the other animals warned that they might possibly unite against the wolves unless some reason was given for the destruction of the rabbits. So the wolves gave them one. 'They were trying to escape,' said the wolves, 'and, as you know, this is no world for escapists.'

Moral: Run, don't walk, to the nearest desert island.

The Unicorn in the Garden

Once upon a sunny morning a man who sat in a breakfast nook looked up from his scrambled eggs to see a white unicorn with a golden horn quietly cropping the roses in the garden. The man went up to the bedroom where his wife was still asleep and woke her. 'There's a unicorn in the garden,' he said. 'Eating roses.' She opened one unfriendly eye and looked at him. 'The unicorn is a mythical beast,' she said, and turned her back on him. The man walked slowly downstairs and out into the garden. The unicorn was still there; he was now browsing among the tulips. 'Here, unicorn,' said the man, and he pulled up a lily and gave it to him. The unicorn ate it gravely. With a high heart, because there was a unicorn in his garden, the man went upstairs and roused his wife again. 'The unicorn,' he said, 'ate a lily.' His wife sat up in bed and looked at him, coldly. 'You are a booby,' she said, 'and I am going to have you put in the booby-hatch.' The man, who had never liked the words 'Booby' and 'Booby-hatch,' and who liked them even less on a shining morning when there was a unicorn in the garden , thought for a moment. 'We'll see about that,' he said. He walked over to the door. 'He has a golden horn in the middle of his forehead,' he told her. Then he went back to the garden to watch the unicorn; but the unicorn had gone away. The man sat down among the roses and went to sleep.

As soon as the husband had gone out of the house, the wife got up and dressed as fast as she could. She was very excited and there was a gloat in her eye. She telephoned the police and she telephoned a psychiatrist; she told them to hurry to her house and bring a strait-jacket. When the police and the psychiatrist arrived they sat down in chairs and looked at her, with great interest. 'My husband,' she said, 'saw a unicorn this morning.' The police looked at the psychiatrist and the psychiatrist looked at the police. 'He told me it ate a lily,' she said. The psychiatrist looked at the police and the police looked at the psychiatrist. 'He told me it had a golden horn in the middle of its forehead,' she said. At a solemn signal from the psychiatrist, the police leaped from their chairs and seized the wife. They had a hard time subduing her, for she put up a terrific struggle, but they finally subdued her. Just as they got her into the strait-jacket, the husband came back into the house.

'Did you tell your wife you saw a unicorn?' asked the police. 'Of course not,' said the husband. 'The unicorn is a mythical beast.' 'That's all I wanted to know,' said the psychiatrist. 'Take her away. I'm sorry, sir, but your wife is as crazy as a jay bird.' So they took her away, cursing and screaming, and shut her up in an institution. The husband lived happily ever after.

Moral: Don't count your boobies until they are hatched.

What do you Mean it 'was' Brillig?

I was sitting at my typewriter one afternoon several weeks ago, staring at a piece of blank white paper, when Della walked in. 'They are here with the reeves,' she said. It did not surprise me that they were. With a coloured woman like Della in the house it would not surprise me if they showed up with the toves. In Della's afternoon it is always brillig; she could outgrabe a mome rath on any wabe in the world. Only Lewis Carroll would have understood Della completely. I try hard enough. 'Let them wait a minute,' I said. I got out the big Century Dictionary and put it on my lap and looked up 'reeve.' It is an interesting word, like all of Della's words; I found out that there are four kinds of reeves. 'Are they here with strings of onions?' I asked. Della said they were not. 'Are they here with enclosures or pens for cattle, poultry, or pigs; sheepfolds?' Della said no sir. 'Are they here with administrative officers?' From a little nearer the door Della said no again. 'Then they've got to be here,' I said, 'with some females of the common European sandpiper.' These scenes of ours take as much out of Della as they do out of me, but she is not a woman to be put down by a crazy man with a dictionary. 'They are here with the reeves for the windas,' said Della with brave stubbornnness. Then, of course, I understood what they were there with: they were there with the Christmas wreaths for the windows. 'Oh, *those* reeves!' I said. We were both greatly relieved; we both laughed. Della and I never quite reach the breaking point; we just come close to it.

Della is a New England coloured woman with nothing of the South in her accent; she doesn't say 'd' for 'th' and she pronounces her 'r's. Hearing her talk in the next room, you might not know at first that she was coloured. You might not know till she said some such thing as 'Do you want cretonnes in the soup tonight?' (She makes wonderful cretonnes for the soup.) I have not found out much about Della's words, but I have learned a great deal about her background. She told me one day that she has three brothers and that one of them works into a garage and another works into an incinerator where they burn the refuge. The one that works into the incinerator has been working into it since the Armitage. That's what Della does to you; she gives you incinerator perfectly and then she comes out with the Armitage. I spent most of an hour one afternoon trying to figure out what was wrong with the Armitage; I thought of Armistead and armature and Armentières, and when I finally hit on Armistice it sounded crazy. It still does. Della's third and youngest brother is my favourite; I think he'll be yours, too, and everybody else's. His name is Arthur and it seems that the has just passed, with commendably high grades, his silver-service eliminations. Della is delighted about that, but she is not half so delighted about it as I am.

Della came to our house in Connecticut some months ago, trailing her glory of cloudiness. I can place the date for you approximately: it was while there were still a great many fletchers about. 'The lawn is full of fletchers,' Della told me one morning, shortly after she arrived, when she brought up my orange juice. 'You mean neighbours?' I said. 'This early?' By the way she laughed I knew that fletchers weren't people; at least not people of flesh and blood. I got dressed and went downstairs and looked up the word in the indispensable Century. A fletcher, I found, is a man who makes arrows. I decided, but without a great deal of conviction, that there couldn't be any arrow-makers on my lawn at that hour in the morning and at this particular period in history. I walked cautiously out the back door and around to the front of the house – and there they were. I don't know many birds but I do know flickers. A flicker is a bird which, if it were really named fletcher, would be called flicker by all the coloured cooks in the United States. Out of a mild curiosity I looked up "flicker" in the dictionary and I discovered that he is a bird of several aliases. When Della brought my toast and coffee into the dining room I told her about this. "Fletchers," I said, "are also golden-winged woodpeckers, yellowhammers, and high-holders." For the first time Della gave me the look that I was to recognise later, during the scene about the reeves. I have become very familiar with that look and I believe I know the thoughts that lie behind it. Della was puzzled at first because I work at home instead of in an office, but I think she has it figured out now. This man, she thinks, used to work into an office like anybody else, but he had to be sent to an institution; he got well enough to come home from the institution, but he is still not well enough to go to back to the office. I could have avoided all these suspicions, of course, if I had simply come out in the beginning and corrected Della when she got words wrong. Coming at her obliquely with a dictionary only enriches the confusion; but I wouldn't have it any other way. I share with

Della a form of escapism that is the most mystic and satisfying flight from actuality I have ever known. It may not always comfort me, but it never ceases to beguile me.

Every Thursday when I drive Della to Waterbury in the car for her day off, I explore the dark depths and the strange recesses of her nomenclature. I found out that she had been married for ten years but was now divorced; that is, her husband went away one day and never came back. When I asked her what he did for a living, she said he worked into a dove-wedding. 'Into a what?' I asked. 'Into a dove-wedding,' said Della. It is one of the words I haven't figured out yet, but I am still working on it. 'Where are you from, Mr. Thurl?' she asked me one day. I told her Ohio, and she said, 'Ooooh, to be sure!' as if I had given her a clue to my crazy definitions, my insensitivity to the ordinary household nouns, and my ignorance of the commoner migratory birds. 'Semantics, Ohio,' I said. 'Why, there's one of them in Massachusetts, too,' said Della. 'The one I mean,' I told her, 'is bigger and more confusing.' 'I'll bet it is,' said Della.

Della told me the other day that she had had only one sister, a beautiful girl who died when she was twenty-one. 'That's too bad,' I said. 'What was the matter?' Della had what was the matter at her tongue's tip. 'She got tuberculosis from her teeth,' she said, 'and it went all through her symptom.' I didn't know what to say to that except that my teeth were all right but that my symptom could probably be easily gone all through. 'You work too much with your brain,' said Della. I knew she was trying to draw me out about my brain and what had happened to it so that I could no longer work into an office, but I changed the subject. There is no doubt that Della is considerably worried about my mental condition. One morning when I didn't get up till noon because I had been writing letters until three o'clock, Della told my wife at breakfast what was the matter with me. 'His mind works so fast his body can't keep up with it,' she said. This diagnosis has shaken me not a little. I have decided to sleep longer and work less. I know exactly what will happen to me if my mind gets so far ahead of my body that my body can't catch up with it. They will come with a reeve and this time it won't be a red-and-green one for the window, it will be a black one for the door.

The Macbeth Murder Mystery

'It was a stupid mistake to make,' said the American woman I had met at my hotel in the English lake country, 'but it was on the counter with the other Penguin books – the little sixpenny ones, you know, with the paper covers – and I supposed of course it was a detective story. All the others were detective stories. I'd read all the others, so I bought this one without really looking at it carefully. You can imagine how mad I was when I found it was Shakespeare.' I murmured something sympathetically. 'I don't see why the Penguin-books people had to get out Shakespeare's plays in the same size and everything as the detective stories,' went on my companion. 'I think they have different-coloured jackets,' I said. 'Well, I didn't notice that,' she said. 'Anyway, I got real comfy in bed that night and all ready to read a good mystery story and here I had "The Tragedy of Macbeth" – a book for high-school students. Like "Ivanhoe." ' 'Or "Lorna Doone",' I said. 'Exactly,' said the American lady. 'And I was just crazy for a good Agatha Christie, or something. Hercule Poirot is my favourite detective.' 'Is he the rabbity one?' I asked. 'Oh, no,' said my crime-fiction expert. 'He's the Belgian one. You're thinking of Mr Pinkerton, the one that helps Inspector Bull. He's good, too.'

Over her second cup of tea my companion began to tell the plot of a detective story that had fooled her completely – it seems it was the old family doctor all the time. But I cut in on her. 'Tell me,' I said. 'Did you read "Macbeth"?' 'I *had* to read it,' she said. 'There wasn't a scrap of anything else to read in the whole room.' 'Did you like it?' I asked. 'No, I did not,' she said, decisively. 'In the first place, I don't think for a moment that Macbeth did it.' I looked at her blankly. 'Did what?' I asked. 'I don't think for a moment that he killed the King,' she said. 'I don't think the Macbeth woman was mixed up in it, either. You suspect them the most, of course, but those are the ones that are never guilty – or shouldn't be, anyway.' 'I'm afraid,' I began, 'that I—' 'But don't you see?' said the American lady. 'It would spoil everything if you could figure out right away who did it. Shakespeare was too smart for that. I've read that people never *have* figured out "Hamlet", so it isn't likely Shakespeare would have made "Macbeth" as simple as it seems.' I thought this over while I filled my pipe. 'Who do you suspect?' I asked, suddenly. 'Macduff,' she said, promptly. 'Good God!' I whispered, softly.

'Oh, Macduff did it, all right,' said the murder specialist. 'Hercule Poirot would have got him easily.' 'How did you figure it out?' I demanded. 'Well,' she said, 'I didn't right away. At first I suspected Banquo. And then, of course, he was the second person killed. That was good right in there, that part. The person you suspect of the first murder should always be the second victim.' 'Is that so?' I murmured. 'Oh, yes,' said my informant. 'They have to keep surprising you. Well, after the second murder I didn't know *who* the killer was for a while.' 'How about Malcolm and Donalbain, the King's sons?' I asked. 'As I remember it, they fled right after the first murder. That looks suspicious.' 'Too suspicious,' said the American lady. 'Much too suspicious. When they flee, they're never guilty. You can count on that.' 'I believe,' I said, 'I'll have a brandy,' and I summoned the waiter. My companion leaned toward me, her eyes bright, her teacup quivering. 'Do you know who discovered Duncan's body?' she demanded. I said I was sorry, but I had forgotten. 'Macduff discovers it,' she said, slipping into the historical present. 'Then he comes running downstairs and shouts, "Confusion has broke open the Lord's anointed temple" and "Sacrilegious murder has made his masterpiece" and on and on like that.' The good lady tapped me on the knee. 'All that stuff was *rehearsed*,' she said. 'You wouldn't say a lot of stuff like that, offhand, would you – if you had found a body?' She fixed me with a glittering eye. 'I—' I began. 'You're right!' she said. 'You wouldn't! Unless you had practised it in advance. "My God, there's a body in here!" is what an innocent man would say.' She sat back with a confident glare.

I thought for a while. 'But what do you make of the Third Murderer?' I asked. 'You know, the Third Murderer has puzzled "Macbeth" scholars for three hundred years.' 'That's because they never thought of Macduff,' said the American lady. 'It was Macduff, I'm certain. You couldn't have one of the victims murdered by two ordinary thugs – the murderer always has to be somebody important.' 'But what about the banquet scene?' I asked, after a moment. 'How do you account for Macbeth's guilty actions there, when Banquo's ghost came in and sat in his chair?' The lady leaned forward and tapped me on the knee again. 'There wasn't any ghost,' she said, 'A big, strong man like that doesn't go around seeing ghosts – especially in a brightly lighted banquet hall with dozens of people around. Macbeth was *shielding some-body!*' 'Who was he shielding?' I asked. 'Mrs Macbeth, of course,' she said. 'He thought she did it and he was going to take the rap himself. The husband always does that when the wife is sus-pected.' 'But what,' I demanded, 'about the sleepwalking scene, then?' 'The same thing, only the other way around,' said my companion. 'That time *she* was shielding *him*. She wasn't asleep at all. Do you remember where it says, ''Enter Lady Macbeth with a taper''?' 'Yes,' I said. 'Well, people who walk in their sleep *never carry lights!*' said my fellow-traveller. 'They have a second sight. Did you ever hear of a sleepwalker carrying a light?' 'No,' I said, 'I never did.' 'Well, then, she wasn't asleep. She was acting guilty to shield Macbeth.' 'I think,' I said, 'I'll have another brandy,' and I called the waiter. When he brought it, I drank it rapidly and rose to go. 'I believe,' I said, 'that you have got hold of something. Would you lend me that ''Macbeth''? I'd like to look it over tonight. I don't feel, somehow, as if I'd ever really read it.' 'I'll get it for you,' she said. 'But you'll find that I am right.'

I read the play over carefully that night, and the next morning, after breakfast, I sought out the American woman. She was on the putting green, and I came up behind her silently and took her arm. She gave an exclamation. 'Could I see you alone?' I asked, in a low voice. She nodded cautiously and followed me to a secluded spot. 'You've found out something?' she breathed. 'I've found out,' I said, triumphantly, 'the name of the murderer!' 'You mean it wasn't Macduff?' she said. 'Macduff is as innocent of those mur-ders,' I said, 'as Macbeth and the Macbeth woman.' I opened the copy of the play, which I had with me, and turned to Act II, Scene 2. 'Here,' I said. 'you will see where Lady Macbeth says, ''I laid their daggers ready. He could not miss 'em. Had he not resembled my father as he slept, I had done it.'' Do you see?' 'No,' said the American woman, bluntly, 'I don't.' 'But it's simple!' I exclaimed. 'I wonder I didn't see it years ago. The reason Duncan resembled Lady Macbeth's father as he slept is that *it actually was her father!*' 'Good God!' breathed my companion, softly. 'Lady Macbeth's father killed the King,' I said, 'and, hearing someone coming, thrust the body under the bed and crawled into the bed himself.' 'But,' said the lady, 'you can't have a murderer who only appears in the story once. You can't have that.' 'I know that,' I said, and I turned to Act II, Scene 4. 'It says here, ''Enter Ross with an old Man.'' Now, that old man is never identified and it is my conten-tion he was old Mr Macbeth, whose ambition it was to make his daughter Queen. There you have your motive.' 'But even then,' cried the American lady, 'he's still a minor character!' 'Not,' I said, gleefully, 'when you realise that he was also *one of the weird sisters in disguise!*' 'You mean one of the three witches?' 'Precisely,' I said. 'Listen to this speech of the old man's. "On Tuesday last, a falcon towering in her pride of place, was by a mousing owl hawk'd at and kill'd.' Who does that sound like?' 'It sounds like the way the three witches talk,' said my companion, reluctantly. 'Precisely!' I said again. 'Well,' said the American woman, 'maybe you're right, but—' 'I'm sure I am,' I said. 'And do you know what I'm going to do now?' 'No,' she said. 'What?' 'Buy a copy of "Hamlet",' I said, 'and solve *that*!' My companion's eyes brightened. 'Then,' she said, 'you don't think Hamlet did it?' 'I am,' I said, 'absolutely positive he didn't.' 'But who,' she demanded, 'do you suspect?' I looked at her cryptically. 'Everybody,' I said, and disappeared into a small grove of trees as silently as I had come.

The Secret Life of Walter Mitty

'We're going through!' The Commander's voice was like thin ice breaking. He wore his full-dress uniform, with the heavily braided white cap pulled down rakishly over one cold grey eye. 'We can't make it, sir. It's spoiling for a hurricane, if you ask me.' 'I'm not asking you, Lieutenant Berg,' said the Commander. 'Throw on the power lights! Rev her up to 8,500! We're going through!' The pounding of the cylinders increased: ta-pocketa-pocketa-pocketa-*pocketa-pocketa*. The Commander stared at the ice forming on the pilot window. He walked over and twisted a row of complicated dials. 'Switch on No. 8 auxiliary!' he shouted. 'Switch on No. 8 auxiliary!' repeated Lieutenant Berg. 'Full strength in No. 3 turret!' shouted the Commander.' Full strength in No. 3 turret!' The crew, bending to their various tasks in the huge, hurtling eight-engined Navy hydroplane, looked at each other and grinned. 'The Old Man'll get us through,' they said to one another. 'The Old Man ain't afraid of Hell!' . . .

'Not so fast! You're driving too fast!' said Mrs Mitty. 'What are you driving so fast for?'

'Hmm?' said Walter Mitty. He looked at his wife, in the seat beside him, with shocked astonishment. She seemed grossly unfamiliar, like a strange woman who had yelled at him in a crowd. 'You were up to fifty-five,' she said. 'You know I don't like to go more than forty. You were up to fifty-five.' Walter Mitty drove on toward Waterbury in silence, the roaring of the SN202 through the worst storm in twenty years of Navy flying fading in the remote, intimate airways of his mind. 'You're tensed up again,' said Mrs Mitty. 'It's one of your days. I wish you'd let Dr Renshaw look you over.'

Walter Mitty stopped the car in front of the building where his wife went to have her hair done. 'Remember to get those overshoes while I'm having my hair done,' she said. 'I don't need overshoes,' said Mitty. She put her mirror back into her bag. 'We've been all through that,' she said, getting out of the car. 'You're not a young man any longer.' He raced the engine a little. 'Why don't you wear your gloves? Have you lost your gloves?' Walter Mitty reached in a pocket and brought out the gloves. He put them on, but after she had turned and gone into the building and he had driven on to a red light, he took them off again. 'Pick it up, brother!' snapped a cop as the light changed, and Mitty hastily pulled on his gloves and lurched ahead. He drove around the streets aimlessly for a time, and then he drove past the hospital on his way to the parking lot.

. . . 'It's the millionaire banker, Wellington McMillan,' said the pretty nurse. 'Yes?' said Walter Mitty, removing his gloves slowly. 'Who has the case?' 'Dr Renshaw and Dr Benbow, but there are two specialists here, Dr Remington from New York and Mr Pritchard-Mitford from London. He flew over.' A door opened down a long, cool corridor and Dr Renshaw came out. He looked distraught and haggard. 'Hello, Mitty,' he said. 'We're having the devil's own time with McMillan, the millionaire banker and close personal friend of Roosevelt. Obstreosis of the ductal tract. Tertiary. Wish you'd take a look at him.' 'Glad to,' said Mitty.

In the operating room there were whispered introductions: 'Dr Remington, Dr Mitty. Mr Pritchard-Mitford, Dr Mitty.' 'I've read your book on streptothricosis,' said Pritchard-Mitford, shaking hands. 'A brilliant performance, sir.' 'Thank you,' said Walter Mitty. 'Didn't know you were in the States, Mitty,' grumbled Remington. 'Coals to Newcastle, bringing Mitford and me up here for a tertiary.' 'You are very kind,' said Mitty. A huge, complicated machine, connected to the operating table, with many tubes and wires, began at this moment to go pocketa-pocketa-pocketa. 'The new anæsthetiser is giving way!' shouted an interne. 'There is no one in the East who knows how to fix it!' 'Quiet, man!' said Mitty, in a low, cool voice. He sprang to the machine, which was now going pocketa-pocketa-queep-pocketa-queep. He began fingering delicately a row of glistening dials. 'Give me a fountain pen!' he snapped. Someone handed him a fountain pen. He pulled a faulty piston out of the machine and inserted the pen in its place. 'That will hold for ten minutes,' he said. 'Get on with the operation.' A nurse hurried over and whispered to Renshaw, and Mitty saw the man turn pale. 'Coreopsis has set in,' said Renshaw nervously. 'If you would take over, Mitty?' Mitty looked at him and at the craven figure of Benbow, who drank, and at the grave, uncertain faces of the two great specialists. 'If you wish,' he said. They slipped a white gown on him; he adjusted a mask and drew on thin gloves; nurses handed him shining . . .

'Back it up, Mac! Look out for that Buick!' Walter Mitty jammed on the brakes. 'Wrong lane, Mac,' said the parking-lot attendant, looking at Mitty closely. 'Gee. Yeh,' muttered Mitty. He began cautiously to back out of the lane marked 'Exit Only.' 'Leave her sit there,' said the attendant. 'I'll put her away.' Mitty got out of the car. 'Hey, better leave the key.' 'Oh,' said Mitty, handing the man the ignition key. The attendant vaulted into the car, backed it up with insolent skill, and put it where it belonged.

They're so damn cocky, thought Walter Mitty, walking along Main Street; they think they know everything. Once he had tried to take his chains off, outside New Milford, and he had got them wound around the axles. A man had had to come out in a wrecking car and unwind them, a young, grinning garageman. Since then Mrs Mitty always made him drive to a garage to have the chains taken off. The next time, he thought, I'll wear my right arm in a sling; they won't grin at me then. I'll have my right arm in a sling and they'll see I couldn't possibly take the chains off myself. He kicked at the slush on the sidewalk. 'Overshoes,' he said to himself, and he began looking for a shoe store.

When he came out into the street again, with the overshoes in a box under his arm, Walter Mitty began to wonder what the other thing was his wife had told him to get. She had told him, twice, before they set out from their house for Waterbury. In a way he hated these weekly trips to town – he was always getting something wrong. Kleenex, he thought, Squibb's, razor blades? No. Toothpaste, toothbrush, bicarbonate, carborundum, initiative and referendum? He gave it up. But she would remember it. 'Where's the what's-its-name?' she would ask. 'Don't tell me you forgot the what's-its-name.' A newsboy went by shouting something about the Waterbury trial.

. . . 'Perhaps this will refresh your memory.' The District Attorney suddenly thrust a heavy automatic at the quiet figure on the witness stand. 'Have you ever seen this before?' Walter Mitty took the gun and examined it expertly. 'This is my Webley-Vickers 50.80,' he said calmly. An excited buzz ran around the courtroom. The Judge rapped for order. 'You are a crack shot with any sort of firearms, I believe?' said the District Attorney, insinuatingly. 'Objection!' shouted Mitty's attorney. 'We have shown that the defendant could not have fired the shot. We have shown that he wore his right arm in a sling on the night of the fourteenth of July.' Walter Mitty raised his hand briefly and the bickering attorneys were stilled. 'With any known make of gun,' he said evenly, 'I could have killed Gregory Fitzhurst at three hundred feet *with my left hand*.' Pandemonium broke loose in the courtroom. A woman's scream rose above the bedlam and suddenly a lovely, dark-haired girl was in Walter Mitty's arms. The District Attorney struck at her savagely. Without rising from his chair, Mitty let the man have it on the point of the chin. 'You miserable cur!' . . .

'Puppy biscuit,' said Walter Mitty. He stopped walking and the buildings of Waterbury rose up out of the misty courtroom and surrounded him again. A woman who was passing laughed. 'He said "Puppy biscuit",' she said to her companion. 'The man said "Puppy biscuit" to himself.' Walter Mitty hurried on. He went into an A. & P., not the first one he came to but a smaller one farther up the street 'I want some biscuit for small, young dogs,' he said to the clerk. 'Any special brand, sir?' The greatest pistol shot in the world thought a moment. 'It says "Puppies Bark for It" on the box,' said Walter Mitty.

His wife would be through at the hairdresser's in fifteen minutes, Mitty saw in looking at his watch, unless they had trouble drying it; sometimes they had trouble drying it. She didn't like to get to the hotel first; she would want him to be there waiting for her as usual. He found a big leather chair in the lobby, facing a window, and he put the overshoes and the puppy biscuit on the floor beside it. He picked up an old copy of *Liberty* and sank down into the chair. 'Can Germany Conquer the World Through the Air?' Walter Mitty looked at the pictures of bombing planes and of ruined streets.

. . . 'The cannonading has got the wind up in young Raleigh, sir,' said the sergeant. Captain Mitty looked up at him through touseled hair. 'Get him to bed,' he said wearily. 'With the others. I'll fly alone.' 'But you can't, sir,' said the sergeant anxiously. 'It takes two men to handle that bomber and the Archies are pounding hell out of the air. Von Richtman's circus is between here and Saulier.' 'Somebody's got to get that ammunition dump,' said Mitty. 'I'm going over. Spot of brandy?' He poured a drink for the sergeant and one for himself. War thundered and whined around the dugout and battered at the door. There was a rending of wood and splinters flew through the room. 'A bit of a near thing,' said Captain Mitty carelessly. 'The box barrage is closing in,' said the sergeant. 'We only live once, Sergeant,' said Mitty, with his faint, fleeting smile. 'Or do we?' He poured another brandy and tossed it off. 'I never see a man could hold his brandy like you, sir,' said the sergeant. 'Begging your pardon, sir.' Captain Mitty stood up and strapped on his huge Webley-Vickers automatic. 'It's forty kilometres through hell, sir,' said the sergeant. Mitty finished one last brandy. 'After all,' he said softly, 'what isn't?' The pounding of the cannon increased; there was the rat-tat-tatting of machine guns, and from somewhere came the menacing pocketa-pocketa-pocketa of the new flame-throwers. Walter Mitty walked to the door of the dugout humming 'Auprès de Ma Blonde.' He turned and waved to the sergeant. 'Cheerio!' he said . . .

Something struck his shoulder. 'I've been looking all over this hotel for you,' said Mrs Mitty. 'Why do you have to hide in this old chair? How did you expect me to find you?' 'Things close in,' said Walter Mitty vaguely. 'What?' Mrs Mitty said. 'Did you get the what's-its-name? The puppy biscuit? What's in that box?' 'Over-shoes,' said Mitty. 'Couldn't you have put them on in the store?' 'I was thinking,' said Walter Mitty. 'Does it ever occur to you that I am sometimes thinking?' She looked at him. 'I'm going to take your temperature when I get you home,' she said.

They went out through the revolving doors that made a faintly derisive whistling sound when you pushed them. It was two blocks to the parking lot. At the drugstore on the corner she said, 'Wait here for me. I forgot something. I won't be a minute.' She was more than a minute. Walter Mitty lighted a cigarette. It began to rain, rain with sleet in it. He stood up against the wall of the drugstore, smoking . . . He put his shoulders back and his heels together. 'To hell with the handkerchief,' said Walter Mitty scorn-fully. He took one last drag on his cigarette and snapped it away. Then, with that faint, fleeting smile playing about his lips, he faced the firing squad; erect and motionless, proud and disdainful, Walter Mitty the Undefeated, inscrutable to the last.

Memorial

She came all the way from Illinois by train in a big wooden crate 13 years ago, a frightened black poodle, not yet a year old. She felt terrible in body and worse in mind. These contraptions that men put on wheels, in contravention of that law of nature which holds that the feet must come in contact with the ground in travelling, dismayed her. She was never able to ride 1000 yards in an automobile without getting sick at her stomach, but she was always apologetic about this frailty, never, as she might well have been, reproachful.

She tried patiently at all times to understand Man's way of life: the rolling of his wheels, the raising of his voice, the ringing of his bells; his way of searching out with lights the dark protecting corners of the night; his habit of building his beds inside walls, high above the nurturing earth. She refused, with all courtesy, to accept his silly notion that it is better to bear puppies in a place made of machined wood and clean blue cloth than in the dark and warm dirt beneath the oak flooring of the barn.

The poodle was hand in glove with natural phenomena. She raised two litters of puppies, 11 each time, taking them in her stride, the way she took the lightning and the snow. One of these litters, which arrived ahead of schedule, was discovered under the barn floor by a little girl of 4. The child gaily displayed on her right forearm the almost invisible and entirely painless marks of teeth which had gently induced her to put down the live black toys she had found and wanted to play with.

The poodle had no vices that I can think of, unless you could count her incurable appetite for the tender tips of the young asparagus in the garden and for the black raspberries when they ripened on the bushes in the orchard. Sometimes, as punishment for her depredations, she walked into bees' nests or got her long shaggy ears tangled in fence wire. She never snarled about the penalties of existence or whimpered about the trials and grotesqueries of life with Man.

She accepted gracefully the indignities of the clipping machine which, in her maiden days, periodically made a clown of her for the dog shows, in accordance with the stupid and unimaginative notion, inherited from the drunken Romans, that this most sensitive and dignified of animals is at heart a fool. The poodle, which can look as husky as a Briard when left shaggy, is an outdoors dog and can hold its own in the field with the best of the retrievers, including the Labrador.

The poodle won a great many ribbons in her bench days, and once went best of breed at Madison Square Garden, but she would have traded all her medals for a dish of asparagus. She knew it was show time when a red rubber bib was tied around her neck. That meant a ride in a car. I used to ride with her in the rumble seat, and once, on our way to Newport, when the rain came down suddenly, there was I with one hand on the poodle's shoulder and the other holding over her a bright green parasol. The highways of New England have, I am sure, seldom beheld a more remarkable sight.

Like the Great Gammeyer of Tarkington's *Gentle Julia*, the poodle I knew seemed sometimes about to bridge the mysterious and conceivably narrow gap that separates instinct from reason. She could take part in your gaiety and your sorrow; she trembled to your uncertainties and lifted her head at your assurances. There were times when she seemed to come close to a pitying comprehension of the whole troubled scene and what lies ticking behind it. If poodles, who walk so easily upon their hind legs, ever do learn the little tricks of speech and reason, I should not be surprised if they made a better job of it than Man, who would seem to be slowly slipping back to all fours, in spite of Van Wyck Brooks and Lewis Mumford and Robert Frost.

The poodle kept her sight, her hearing, and her figure up to her quiet and dignified end. She knew that the Hand was upon her and she accepted it with a grave and unapprehensive resignation. This, her dark intelligent eyes seemed to be trying to tell me, is simply the closing of full circle, this is the flower that grows out of Beginning; this – not to make it too hard for you, friend – is as natural as eating the raspberries and raising the puppies and riding into the rain.

A Ride with Olympy

Olympy Sementzoff called me 'Monsieur' because I was the master of the Villa Tamisier and he was the gardener, the Russian husband of the French caretaker, Maria. I called him 'Monsieur,' too, because I could never learn to call any man Olympy and because there was a wistful air of *ancien régime* about him. He drank Bénédictine with me and smoked my cigarettes; he also, as you will see, drove my car. We conversed in French, a language alien to both of us, but more alien to me than to him. He said 'gauche' for both 'right' and 'left' when he was upset, but when I was upset I was capable of flights that put the French people on their guard, wide-eyed and wary. Once, for instance, when I cut my wrist on a piece of glass I ran into the lobby of a hotel shouting in French, 'I am sick with a knife!' Olympy would have known what to say (except that it would have been his left wrist in any case) but he wouldn't have shouted: his words ran softly together and sounded something like the burbling of water over stones. Often I did not know what he was talking about; rarely did he know what I was talking about. There was misty, faraway quality about this relationship, in French, of Russia and Ohio. The fact that the accident Olympy and I were involved in fell short of catastrophe was, in view of everything, something of a miracle.

Olympy and Maria 'came with' the villa my wife and I rented on Cap d'Antibes. Maria was a deep-bosomed, large-waisted woman, as persistently pleasant as Riviera weather in a good season; no mistral ever blew in the even climate of her temperament. She must have been more than forty-five but she was as strong as a root; once when I had trouble getting a tought cork out of a wine bottle she took hold and whisked it out as if it had been a maidenhair fern. On Sundays her son came over from the barracks in Antibes and we all had a glass of white Bordeaux together, sometimes the Sementzoffs' wine, sometimes our own. Her son was eighteen and a member of the Sixth Regiment of Chasseurs Alpins, a tall, sombre boy, handsome in his uniform and cape. He was an *enfant du premier lit,* as the French say. Maria made her first bed with a sergeant of the army who was *cordonnier* for his regiment during the war and seemed somehow to have laid by quite a little money. After the war the sergeant-shoemaker resigned from the army, put his money in investments of some profoundly mysterious nature in Indo-China, and lost it all. '*Il est mort,*' Maria told us, '*de chagrin.*' Grief over his ill-fortune brought on a decline; the *chagrin,* Maria said, finally reached his brain, and he died at the age of thirty-eight. Maria had to sell their house to pay the taxes, and go to work.

Olympy Sementzoff, Maria's second husband, was shy, not very tall, and wore a beard; in his working clothes you didn't notice much more than that. When he dressed for Sunday – he wore a fine double-breasted jacket – you observed that his mouth was sensitive, his eyes attractively sad, and that he wore his shyness with a certain air. He worked in a boat factory over near Cannes – Maria said that he was a *spécialiste de bateaux,* odd jobs about the villa grounds he did on his off days. It was scarcely light when he got up in the morning, for he had to be at work at seven; it was almost dark when he got home. He was paid an incredibly small amount for what he did at the factory and a handful of sous each month for what he did about the grounds. When I gave him a hundred francs for some work he had done for me in the house – he could repair anything from a drain to a watch – he said, '*Oh, monsieur, c'est trop!*' '*Mais non, monsieur,*' said I. '*Ce n'est pas beaucoup.*' He took it finally, after an exchange of bows and compliments.

The elderly wife of the Frenchman from whom we rented the villa told us, in a dark whisper, that Olympy was a White Russian and that there was perhaps a *petit mystère* about him, but we figured this as her own fanciful bourgeois alarm. Maria did not make a mystery out of her husband. There was the Revolution, most of Olympy's brothers and sisters were killed – one knew how that was – and he escaped. He was, of course, an exile and must not go back. If she knew just who he was in Russia and what he had done, she didn't make it very clear. He was in Russia and he escaped; she had married him thirteen years before; *et puis, voilà!* It would have been nice to believe that there was the blood of the Czars in Olympy, but if there was anything to the ancient legend that all the stray members of the Imperial House took easily and naturally to driving a taxi, that let Olympy out. He was not a born chauffeur, as I found out the day I came back from our automobile ride on foot and – unhappily for Maria – alone.

Olympy Sementzoff rode to and from his work in one of those bastard agglomerations of wheels, motor and superstructure that one saw only in France. It looked at first glance like the cockpit of a cracked-up plane. Then you saw that there were two wheels in front and a single wheel in back. Except for the engine – which Maria said was a 'Morgan *moteur*' – and the wheels and tyres, it was handmade. Olympy's boss at the boat factory had made most of it, but Olympy himself had put on the *ailes*, or fenders, which were made of some kind of wood. The strange canopy that served as a top was Maria's proud handiwork; it seemed to have been made of canvas and kitchen aprons. The thing had a right-hand drive. When the *conducteur* was in his seat he was very low to the ground: you had to bend down to talk to him. There was a small space beside the driver in which another person could sit, or crouch. The whole affair was not much larger than an overturned cabinet victrola. It got bouncingly under way with all the racket of a dog fight and in full swing was capable of perhaps thirty miles an hour. The contraption had cost Olympy three thousand francs, or about a hundred dollars. He had driven it for three years and was hand in glove with its mysterious mechanism. The gadgets on the dash and on the floorboard, which he pulled or pushed to make the things go, seemed to include fire tongs, spoons, and door-knobs. Maria miraculously managed to squeeze into the seat beside the driver in an emergency, but I could understand why she didn't want to drive to the Nice Carnival in the 'Morgan.' It was because she didn't that I suggested Olympy should take her over one day in my Ford sedan. Maria had given us to understand that her *mari* could drive any car – he could be a chauffeur if he wanted to, a *bon* chauffeur. All I would have to do, *voyez-vous*, was to take Olympy for a turn around the Cap so that he could get the hang of the big car. Thus is was that one day after lunch we set off.

Half a mile out of Antibes on the shore road, I stopped the car and changed places with Olympy, letting the engine run. Leaning forward, he took a tense grip on a steering wheel much larger than he was used to and too far away from him. I could see that he was nervous. He put his foot on the clutch, tentatively, and said, '*Embrayage?*' He had me there. My knowledge of French automotive terms is inadequate and volatile. I was forced to say I didn't know. I couldn't remember the word for clutch in any of the three languages, French, Italian and German, in which it was given in my 'Motorist's Guide' (which was back at the villa). Somehow '*embrayage*' didn't sound right for clutch (it is though). I knew it wouldn't do any good for an American writer to explain in French to a Russian boat specialist the purpose that particular pedal served; furthermore, I didn't really know. I compromised by putting my left foot on the brake. *'Frein,'* I said. *'Ah,'* said Olympy, unhappily. This method of indicating what something might be by demonstrating what it wasn't had a disturbing effect. I shifted my foot to the accelerator – or rather pointed my toe at it – and suddenly the word for that, even the French for gasoline, left me. I was growing a little nervous myself. *'Benzina,'* I said, in Italian, finally. *'Ah?'* said Olympy. Whereas we had been one remove from reality to begin with, we were now two, or perhaps three, removes. A polyglot approach to the fine precision of a gas engine is roundabout and dangerous. We both lost a little confidence in each other. I suppose we should have given up right then, but we didn't.

Olympy decided the extra pedal was the *embrayage,* shifted into low from neutral, and the next thing I knew we were making a series of short forward bounds like a rabbit leaping out of a wheat field to see where he is. This form of locomotion takes a lot out of man and car. The engine complained in loud, rhythmic whines. And then Olympy somehow got his left foot on the starter and there was a familiar undertone of protest; this set his right foot to palpitating on the accelerator and the rabbit-jumps increased in scope. Abandoning my search for the word for starter, I grabbed his left knee and shouted *'Ça commence!'* Just what was commencing Olympy naturally couldn't figure – probably some habitual and ominous idiosyncrasy of the machinery. He gave me a quick, pale look. I shut off the ignition, and we discussed the starter situation, breathing a little heavily. He understood what it was, finally, and presently we were lurching ahead again, Olympy holding her in low gear, like a wrestler in a clinch, afraid to risk shifting into second. He tried it at last and with a jamming jolt and a roar we went into reverse: the car writhed like a tortured leopard and the engine quit.

I was puzzled and scared, and so was Olympy. Only a foolish pride in masculine fortitude kept us going. I showed him the little jog to the right of you have to make to shift into second and he started the engine and we were off again, jolting and lurching. He made the shift, finally, with a noise like lightning striking a foundry – and veered swoopingly to the right. We barely missed a series of staunch granite blocks, set in concrete, that mark ditches and soft shoulders. We whisked past a pole. The leaves of a vine hanging on a wall slapped at me through the window. My voice left me. I was fascinated and paralysed by the swift passes disaster was making at my head. At length I was able to grope blindly toward the ignition switch, but got my wrist on the klaxon button. When I jerked my arm away, Olympy began obediently sounding the horn. We were riding on the edge of a ditch. I managed somehow to shut off the ignition and we rolled to a stop. Olympy, unused to a left-hand drive, had forgotten there was a large portion of the car to his right, with me in it. I told him, 'A gauche, à gauche, toujours à gauche!' 'Ah,' said Olympy, but there was no comprehension in him. I could see he didn't know we had been up against the vines of villa walls: intent on the dark problem of gearshifting, he had been oblivious of where the car and I had been. There was a glint in his eye now. He was determined to get the thing into high on his next attempt; we had come about half a mile in the lower gears.

The road curved downhill as it passed Eden Roc and it was here that an elderly English couple, unaware of the fact that hell was loose on the highway, were walking. Olympy was in second again, leaning forward like a racing bicycle rider. I shouted at him to look out, he said 'Oui' – and we grazed the old man and his wife. I glanced back in horror: they were staring at us, mouths and eyes wide, unable to move or make a sound. Olympy raced on to a new peril: a descending hairpin curve, which he negotiated in some far-fetched manner, with me hanging onto the emergency brake. The road straightened out, I let go the brake, and Olympy slammed into high with the desperate gesture of a man trying to clap his hat over a poised butterfly. We began to whiz: Olympy hadn't counted on a fast pickup. He whirled around a car in front of us with a foot to spare. 'Lentement!' I shouted, and then 'Gauche!' as I began to get again the whimper of poles and walls in my ears. 'Ça va mieux, maintenant,' said Olympy, quietly. A wild thought ran through my head that maybe this was the way they used to drive in Russia in the old days.

Ahead of us now was one of the most treacherous curves on the Cap. The road narrowed and bent, like a croquet wicket, around a high stone wall that shut off your view of what was coming. What was coming was usually on the wrong side of the road, so it wouldn't do to shout 'Gauche!' now. We made the turn all right. there was a car coming, but it was well over on its own side. Olympy apparently didn't think so. He whirled the wheel to the right, didn't take up the play fast enough in whirling it back, and there was a tremendous banging crash, like a bronze monument falling. I had a glimpse of Olympy's right hand waving around like the hand of a man hunting for something under a table. I didn't know what his feet were doing. We were still moving, heavily, with a ripping noise and a loud roar. *'Poussez le phare!'* I shouted, which means 'push the headlight!' *'Ah-h-h-h,'* said Olympy. I shut off the ignition and pulled on the hand brake, but we had already stopped. We got out and looked at the pole we had sideswiped and at the car. The right front fender was crumpled and torn and the right back one banged up, but nothing else had been hurt. Olympy's face was so stricken when he looked at me that I felt I had to cheer him up. *'Il fait beau,'* I announced, which is to say that the weather is fine. It was all I could think of.

I started for a garage that Olympy knew about. At the first street we came to he said *'Gauche'* and I turned left. *'Ah, non,'* said Olympy. *'Gauche,'* and he pointed the other way. 'You mean *droit?'* I asked, just that way. *'Ah!'* said Olympy. *'C'est bien ça!'* It was as if he had thought of something he hadn't been able to remember for days. That explained a great deal.

I left Olympy and the car at the garage; he said he would walk back. One of the garage men drove me into Juan-les-Pins and I walked home from there – and into a look of wild dismay in Maria's eyes. I hadn't thought about that: she had seen us drive away together and here I was, alone. *'Où est votre mari?'* I asked her, hurriedly. It was something of a failure as a reassuring beginning. I had taken the question out of her own mouth, so I answered it. 'He has gone for a walk,' I told her. Then I tried to say that her husband was *bon,* but I pronounced it *beau,* so that what I actually said was that her husband was handsome. She must have figured that he was not only dead but laid out. There was a *mauvais quart d'heure* for both of us before the drooping figure of Olympy finally appeared. He explained sadly to Maria that the mechanism of the Ford is strange and curious compared to the mechanism of the Morgan. I agreed with him. Of course, he protested, he would pay for the repairs to the car, but Maria and I both put down that suggestion. Maria's idea of my work was that was paid by the City of New York and enjoyed a tremendous allowance. Olympy got forty francs a day at the boat factory.

That night, at dinner, Maria told us that her *mari* was pacing up and down in their little bedroom at the rear of the house. He was in a state. I didn't want an attack of *chagrin* to come on him as it had on the *cordonnier* and perhaps reach his brain. When Maria was ready to go we gave her a handful of cigarettes for Olympy and a glass of Bénédictine. The next day, at dawn, I heard the familiar

tintamarre and *hurlement* and *brouhaha* of Olympy's wonderful
contraption getting under way once more. He was off to the boat
factory and his forty francs a day, his dollar and thirty cents. It
would have cost him two weeks' salary to pay for the fenders, but
he would have managed it somehow. When I went down to
breakfast, Maria came in from the kitchen with a large volume,
well fingered and full of loose pages, which she handed to me. It
was called *Le Mussée d'Art* and subtitled *Galerie des Chefs-
d'oeuvre et Précis de l'Histoire de l'Art au XIXe Siècle, en France et
à l'Etranger* (*1000 gravures, 58 planches hors texte*). A present to
Monsieur from Olympy Sementzoff, with his compliments. The
incident of the automobile was thus properly rounded off with an
exchange of presents: cigarettes, Bénédictine, and *Le Musée
d'Art*. It seemed to me the way such things should always end, but
perhaps Olympy and I were ahead of our day – or behind it.

There's no Place Like Home

Idling through a London bookstore in the summer of 1937, I came upon a little book called 'Collins' Pocket Interpreters: France.' Written especially to instruct the English how to speak French in the train, the hotel, the quandary, the dilemma, etc., it is, of course, equally useful – I might also say equally depressing – to Americans. I have come across a number of these helps-for-travellers, but none that has the heavy impact, the dark, cumulative power of Collins'. A writer in a London magazine mentions a phrase book got out in the era of Imperial Russia which contained this one magnificent line: 'Oh dear, our postillion has been struck by lightning!' but that fantastic piece of disaster, while charming and provocative – though, I daresay, quite rare even in the days of the Czars – is to Mr Collins' modern, workaday disasters as Fragonard is to George Bellows, or Sarah Orne Jewett to William Faulkner. Let us turn the pages of this appalling little volume.

Each page has a list of English expressions one under the other, which gives them the form of verse. The French translations are run alongside. Thus, on the first page, under 'The Port of Arrival,' we begin (quietly enough) with 'Porter, here is my baggage!' – 'Porteur, voici mes bagages!' From then on disaster follows fast and follows faster until in the end, as you shall see, all hell breaks loose. The volume contains three times as many expressions to use when one is in trouble as when everything is going all right. This, my own experience has shown, is about the right ratio, but God spare me from some of the difficulties for which the traveller is prepared in Mr Collins' melancholy narrative poem. I am going to leave out the French translations because, for one thing, people who get involved in the messes and tangles we are coming to invariably forget their French and scream in English anyway. Furthermore, the French would interrupt the fine, free flow of the English and spoil what amounts to a dramatic tragedy of an overwhelming and original kind. The phrases, as I have said, run one under the other, but herein I shall have to run them one after the other (you can copy them down the other way, if you want to).

Trouble really starts in the canto called 'In the Customs Shed.' Here we have: 'I cannot open my case.' 'I have lost my keys.'

'Help me to close this case.' 'I did not know that I had to pay.' 'I don't want to pay so much.' 'I cannot find my porter.' 'Have you seen porter 153?' That last query is a little master stroke of writing, I think, for in those few words we have a graphic picture of a tourist lost in a jumble of thousands of bags and scores of customs men, looking frantically for one of at least a hundred and fifty-three porters. We feel that the tourist will not find porter 153, and the note of frustration has been struck.

Our tourist (accompanied by his wife, I like to think) finally gets on the the train for Paris – having lost his keys and not having found his porter – and it comes time presently to go ot the dining car, although he probably has no appetite, for the customs men, of course, have had to break open that one suitcase. Now, I think, it is the wife who begins to crumble: 'Someone has taken my seat.' 'Excuse me, sir, that seat is mine.' 'I cannot find my ticket!' 'I have left my ticket in the compartment.' 'I will go and look for it.' 'I have left my gloves (My purse) in the dining car.' Here the note of frenzied disintegration, so familiar to all travellers abroad, is sounded. Next comes 'The Sleeper,' which begins, ominously, with 'What is the matter?' and ends with 'May I open the window?' 'Can you open this window, please?' We realise, of course, that *nobody* is going to be able to open the window and that the tourist and his wife will suffocate. In this condition they arrive in Paris, and the scene there, on the crowded station platform, is done with superb economy of line: 'I have left something in the train.' 'A parcel, an overcoat.' 'A mackintosh, a stick.' 'An umbrella, a camera.' 'A fur, a suitcase.' The travellers have now begun to go completely to pieces, in the grand manner.

Next comes an effective little interlude about an airplane trip, which is one of my favourite passages in this swift and sorrowful tragedy: 'I want to reserve a place in the plane leaving tomorrow morning.' 'When do we start?' 'Can we get anything to eat on board?' 'When do we arrive?' 'I feel sick.' 'Have you any paper bags for air-sickness?' 'The noise is terrible.' 'Have you any cotton wool?' 'When are we going to land?' This brief masterpiece caused me to cancel an air trip from London to Paris and go the easy way, across the Channel.

We now come to a section called 'At the Hotel,' in which things go from worse to awful: 'Did you not get my letter?' 'I wrote to you three weeks ago.' 'I asked for a first-floor room.' 'If you can't give me something better, I shall go away.' 'The chambermaid never comes when I ring.' 'I cannot sleep at night, there is so much noise.' 'I have just had a wire. I must leave at once.' Panic has begun to set in, and it is not appeased any by the advent of 'The Chambermaid': 'Are you the chambermaid?' 'There are no towels here.' 'The sheets on this bed are damp.' 'This room is not clean.' 'I have seen a mouse in the room.' 'You will have to set a mouse trap here.' The bells of hell at this point begin to ring in earnest: 'These shoes are not mine.' 'I put my shoes here, where are they now?' 'The light is not good.' 'The bulb is broken.' 'The radiator is too warm.' 'The radiator doesn't work.' 'It is cold in this room.' 'This is not clean, bring me another.' 'I don't like this.' 'I can't eat this. Take it away!'

I somehow now see the tourist's wife stalking angrily out of the hotel, to get away from it all (without any shoes on), and, properly enough, the booklet seems to follow her course – first under 'Guides and Interpreters': 'You are asking too much.' 'I will not give you any more.' 'I shall call a policeman.' 'He can settle this affair.' Then under 'Inquiring the Way': 'I am lost.' 'I was looking for—' 'Someone robbed me.' 'That man robbed me.' 'That man is following me everywhere.' She rushes to 'The Hairdresser,' where, for a change, everything goes quite smoothly until: 'The water is too hot, you are scalding me!' Then she goes shopping, but there is no surcease: 'You have not given me the right change.' 'I bought this two days ago.' 'It desn't work.' 'It is broken.' 'It is torn.''It doesn't fit me.' Then to a restaurant for a snack and a reviving cup of tea: 'This is not fresh.' 'This piece is too fat.' 'This doesn't smell very nice.' 'There is a mistake in the bill.' 'While I was dining someone has taken my purse.' 'I have left my glasses (my watch) (a ring) in the lavatory.' Madness has now come upon her and she rushes wildly out into the street. Her husband, I think, has at the same time plunged blindly out of the hotel to find her. We come then, quite naturally, to 'Accident,' which is calculated to keep the faint of heart – nay, the heart of oak – safely at home by his own fireside: 'There has been an accident!' 'Go and fetch a policeman quickly.' 'Is there a doctor near here?' 'Send for the ambulance.' 'He is seriously injured.' 'She has been run over.' 'He has been knocked down.' 'Someone has fallen in the water.' 'The ankle, the arm.' 'The back, a bone.' 'The face, the finger.' 'The foot, the head.' 'The knee, the leg.' 'The neck, the nose.' 'The wrist, the shoulder.' 'He has broken his arm.' 'He has broken his leg.' 'He has a sprained ankle.' 'He has a sprained wrist.' 'He is losing blood.' 'He has fainted.' 'He has lost consciousness.' 'He has burnt his face.' 'It is swollen.' 'It is bleeding.' 'Bring some cold water.' 'Help me to carry him.' (Apparently, you just let *her* lie there, while you attend to him – but, of course, she was merely run over, whereas he has taken a terrific tossing around.)

We next see the husband and wife back in their room at the dreary hotel, both in bed, and both obviously hysterical. This scene is entitled 'Illness': 'I am feeling very ill, send for the doctor.' 'I have pains in—' 'I have pains all over.' 'The back, the chest.' 'The ear, the head.' 'The eyes, the heart.' 'The joints, the kidneys.' 'The lungs, the stomach.' 'The throat, the tongue.' 'I feel a pain here.' 'He is not sleeping well.' 'He cannot eat.' 'My stomach is out of order.' 'She is feverish.' 'I have caught a cold.' 'I have caught a chill.' 'He has a temperature.' 'I have a cough.' 'Will you give me a prescription?' 'What must I do?' 'Must I stay in bed?' 'I feel better.' 'When will you come and see me again?' 'Biliousness, rheumatism.' 'Insomnia, sunstroke.' 'Fainting, a fit.' 'Hoarseness, sore throat.' 'The medicine, the remedy.' 'A poultice, a draught.' 'A tablespoonful, a teaspoonful.' 'A sticking plaster, senna.' 'Iodine.' That last suicidal bleat for iodine is, to me, a masterful touch.

Our couple finally get on their feet again, for travellers are tough – they've got to be – but we see under the next heading, 'Common Words and Phrases,' that they are left forever punch-drunk and shattered: 'Can I help you?' 'Excuse me.' 'Carry on!' 'Look here!' 'Look down there!' 'Look up there!' 'Why, how?' 'When, where?' 'Because.' 'That's it!' 'It is too much, it is too dear.' 'It is very cheap.' 'Who, what, which?' 'Look out!' Those are Valkyries, one feels, riding around, and above, and under our unhappy husband and wife. The book sweeps on to a mad operatic ending of the tragedy, with all the strings and brasses and wood winds going full blast: 'Where are we going?' 'Where are you going?' 'Come quickly and see!' 'I shall call a policeman.' 'Bring a policeman!' 'I shall stay here.' 'Will you help me? 'Help! Fire!' 'Who are you?' 'I don't know you.' 'I don't want to speak to you.' 'Leave me alone.' 'That will do.' 'You are mistaken.' 'It was not I.' 'I didn't do it.' 'I will give you nothing.' 'Go away now!' 'It has nothing to do with me.' 'Where should one apply?' 'What must I do?' 'What have I done?' 'I have done nothing.' 'I have already paid you.' 'I have paid you enough.' 'Let me pass!' 'Where is the British consulate?' The oboes take that last, despairing wail, and the curtain comes down.

The Catbird Seat

Mr Martin bought the pack of Camels on Monday night in the most crowded cigar store on Broadway. It was theatre time and seven or eight men were buying cigarettes. The clerk didn't even glance at Mr Martin, who put the pack in his overcoat pocket and went out. If any of the staff at F & S had seen him buy the cigarettes, they would have been astonished, for it was generally known that Mr Martin did not smoke, and never had. No one saw him.

It was just a week to the day since Mr Martin had decided to rub out Mrs Ulgine Barrows. The term 'rub out' pleased him because it suggested nothing more than the correction of an error – in this case an error of Mr Fitweiler. Mr Martin had spent each night of the past week working out his plan and examining it. As he walked home now he went over it again. For the hundredth time he resented the element of imprecision, the margin of guesswork that entered into the business. The project as he had worked it out as casual and bold, the risks were considerable. Something might go wrong anywhere along the line. And therein lay the cunning of his scheme. No one would ever see in it the cautious, painstaking hand of Erwin Martin, head of the filing department at F & S, of whom Mr Fitweiler had once said, 'Man is fallible but Martin isn't.' No one would see his hand, that is, unless it were caught in the act.

Sitting in his apartment, drinking a glass of milk, Mr Martin reviewed his case against Mrs Ulgine Barrows, as he had every night for seven nights. He began at the beginning. Her quacking voice and braying laugh had first profaned the halls of F& S on 7 March 1941 (Mr Martin had a head for dates). Old Roberts, the personnel chief, had introduced her as the newly appointed special adviser to the president of the firm, Mr Fitweiler. The woman had appalled Mr Martin instantly, but he hadn't shown it. He had given her his dry hand, a look of studious concentration, and a faint smile. 'Well,' she had said, looking at the papers on his desk, 'are you lifting the oxcart out of the ditch?' As Mr Martin recalled that moment, over his milk, he squirmed slightly. He must keep his mind on her crimes as a special adviser, not on her peccadillos as a personality. This he found difficult to do, in spite of entering an objection and sustaining it. The faults of the woman as a woman kept chattering on in his mind like an unruly witness. She had, for almost two years now, baited him. In the halls, in the elevator, even in his own office, into which she romped now and then like a circus horse, she was constantly shouting these silly questions at him. 'Are you lifting the oxcart out of the ditch? Are you tearing up the pea patch? Are you hollering down the rain barrel? Are you scraping around the bottom of the pickle barrel? Are you sitting in the catbird seat?'

It was Joey Hart, one of Mr Martin's two assistants, who had explained what the gibberish meant. 'She must be a Dodger fan,' he had said. 'Red Barber announces the Dodger games over the radio and he uses those expressions – picked 'em up down South.' Joey had gone on to explain one or two. 'Tearing up the pea patch' meant going on a rampage; 'sitting in the catbird seat' meant sitting pretty, like a batter with three balls and no strikes on him. Mr Martin dismissed all this with an effort. It had been annoying, it had driven him near to distraction, but he was too solid a man to be moved to murder by anything so childish. It was fortunate, he reflected as he passed on to the important charges against Mrs Barrows, that he had stood up under it so well. He had maintained always an outward appearance of polite tolerance. 'Why, I even believe you like, the woman,' Miss Paird, his other assistant, had once said to him. He had simply smiled.

A gavel rapped in Mr Martin's mind and the case proper was resumed. Mrs Ulgine Barrows stood charged with wilful, blatant, and persistent attempts to destroy the efficiency and system of F & S. It was competent, material, and relevant to review her advent and rise to power. Mr Martin had got the story from Miss Paird, who seemed always able to find things out. According to her, Mrs Barrows had met Mr Fitweiler at a party, where she had rescued him from the embraces of a powerfully built drunken man who had mistaken the president of F & S for a famous retired Middle Western football coach. She had led him to a sofa and somehow worked upon him a monstrous magic. The ageing gentleman had jumped to the conclusion there and then that this was a woman of singular attainments, equipped to bring out the best in him and in the firm. A week later he had introduced her into F & S as his special adviser. On that day confusion got its foot in the door. After Miss Tyson, Mr Brundage, and Mr Bartlett had been fired and Mr Munson had taken his hat and stalked out, mailing in his resignation later, old Roberts had been emboldened to speak to Mr Fitweiler. He mentioned that Mr Munson's department had been 'a little disrupted' and hadn't they perhaps better resume the old system there? Mr Fitweiler had said certainly not. He had the greatest faith in Mrs Barrow's ideas. 'They require a little seasoning, a little seasoning, is all,' he had added. Mr Roberts had given it up. Mr Martin reviewed in detail all the changes wrought by Mrs Barrows. She had begun chipping at the cornices of the firm's edifice and now she was swinging at the foundation stones with a pickaxe.

Mr Martin came now, in his summing up, to the afternoon of Monday, November 2, 1942 – just one week ago. On that day, at 3 P.M., Mrs Barrows had bounced into his office. 'Boo!' she had yelled. 'Are you scraping around the bottom of the pickle barrel?' Mr Martin had looked at her from under his green eyeshade, saying nothing. She had begun to wander about the office, taking it in with her great, popping eyes. 'Do you really need *all* these filing cabinets?' she had demanded suddenly. Mr Martin's heart had jumped. 'Each of these files,' he had said, keeping his voice even, 'plays an indispensable part in the system of F & S.' She had brayed at him, 'Well, don't tear up the pea patch!' and gone to the door. From there she had bawled, 'But you sure have got a lot of fine scrap in here!' Mr Martin could no longer doubt that the finger was on his beloved department. Her pickaxe was on the upswing, poised for the first blow. It had not come yet; he had received no blue memo from the enchanted Mr Fitweiler bearing nonsensical instruction deriving from the obscene woman. But there was no doubt in Mr Martin's mind that one would be forthcoming. He must act quickly. Already a precious week had gone by. Mr Martin stood up in his living room, still holding his milk glass. 'Gentlemen of the jury,' he said to himself, 'I demand the death penalty for this horrible person.'

The next day Mr Martin followed his routine, as usual. He polished his glasses more often and once sharpened an already sharp pencil, but not even Miss Paird noticed. Only once did he catch sight of his victim; she swept past him in the hall with a patronising 'Hi!' At five-thirty he walked home, as usual, and had a glass of milk, as usual. He had never drunk anything stronger in his life – unless you could count ginger ale. The late Sam Schlosser, the S of F & S, had praised Mr Martin at a staff meeting several years before for his temperate habits. 'Our most efficient worker neither drinks nor smokes,' he had said. 'The results speak for themselves.' Mr Fitweiler had sat by, nodding approval.

Mr Martin was still thinking about that red-letter day as he walked over to the Schrafft's on Fifth Avenue near Forty-sixth Street. He got there, as he always did, at eight o'clock. He finished his dinner and the financial page of the *Sun* at a quarter to nine, as he always did. It was his custom after dinner to take a walk. This time he walked down Fifth Avenue at a casual pace. His gloved hands felt moist and warm, his forehead cold. He transferred the Camels from his overcoat to jacket pocket. He wondered, as he did so, if they did not represent an unnecessary note of strain. Mrs Barrows smoked only Luckies. It was his idea to puff a few puffs on a Camel (after the rubbing-out), stub it out in the ashtray holding her lipstick-stained Luckies, and thus drag a small red herring across the trail. Perhaps it was not a good idea. It would take time. He might even choke, too loudly.

Mr Martin had never seen the house on West Twelfth Street where Mrs Barrows lived, but he had a clear enough picture of it. Fortunately, she had bragged to everybody about her ducky first-floor apartment in the perfectly darling three-story red-brick. There would be no door man or other attendants; just the tenants of the second and third floors. As he walked along, Mr Martin realised that he would get there before nine-thirty. He had considered walking north on Fifth Avenue from Schrafft's to a point from which it would take him until ten o'clock to reach the house. At that hour people were less likely to be coming in or going out. But the procedure would have made an awkward loop in the straight thread of his casualness, and he had abandoned it. It was impossible to figure when people would be entering or leaving the house, anyway. There was a great risk at any hour. If he ran into anybody, he would simply have to place the rubbing-out of Ulgine Barrows in the inactive file forever. The same thing would hold true if there were someone in her apartment. In that case he would just say that he had been passing by, recognised her charming house and thought to drop in.

It was eighteen minutes after nine when Mr Martin turned into Twelfth Street. A man passed him, and a man and a woman talking. There was no one within fifty paces when he came to the house, halfway down the block. He was up the steps and in the small vestibule in no time, pressing the bell under the card that said 'Mrs Ulgine Barrows.' When the clicking in the lock started, he jumped forward against the door. He got inside fast, closing the door behind him. A bulb in a lantern hung from the hall ceiling on a chain seemed to give a monstrously bright light. There was nobody on the stair, which went up ahead of him along the left wall. A door opened down the hall in the wall on the right. He went toward it swiftly, on tiptoe.

'Well, for God's sake, look who's here!' bawled Mrs Barrows, and her braying laugh rang out like the report of a shotgun. He rushed past her like a football tackle, bumping her. 'Hey, quit shoving!' she said, closing the door behind them. They were in her living room, which seemed to Mr Martin to be lighted by a hundred lamps. 'What's after you?' she said. 'You're as jumpy as a goat.' He found he was unable to speak. His heart was wheezing in his throat. 'I—yes,' he finally brought out. She was jabbering and laughing as she started to help him off with his coat. 'No, no,' he said. 'I'll put it here.' He took it off and put it on a chair near the door. 'Your hat and gloves, too,' she said. 'You're in a lady's house.' He put his hat on top of the coat. Mrs Barrows seemed larger than he had thought. He kept his gloves on. 'I was passing by,' he said. 'I recognised—is there anyone here?' She laughed louder than ever. 'No,' she said, 'we're all alone. You're as white as a sheet, you funny man. Whatever *has* come over you? I'll mix you a toddy.' She started toward a door across the room. 'Scotch-and-soda be all right? But say, you don't drink, do you?' She turned and gave him her amused look. Mr Martin pulled himself together. 'Scotch-and-soda will be all right,' he heard himself say. He could hear her laughing in the kitchen.

Mr Martin looked quickly around the living room for the weapon. He had counted on finding one there. There were and-irons and a poker and something in a corner that looked like an Indian club. None of them would do. It couldn't be that way. He began to pace around. He came to a desk. On it lay a metal paper knife with an ornate handle. Would it be sharp enough? He reached for it and knocked over a small brass jar. Stamps spilled out of it and it fell to the floor with a clatter. 'Hey,' Mrs Barrows yelled from the kitchen, 'are you tearing up the pea patch?' Mr Martin gave a strange laugh. Picking up the knife, he tried its point against his left wrist. It was blunt. It wouldn't do.

When Mrs Barrows reappeared, carrying two highballs, Mr Martin, standing there with his gloves on, became acutely conscious of the fantasy he had wrought. Cigarettes in his pocket, a drink prepared for him – it was all too grossly improbable. It was more than that; it was impossible. Somewhere in the back of his mind a vague idea stirred, sprouted. 'For heaven's sake, take off those gloves,' said Mrs Barrows. 'I always wear them in the house,' said Mr Martin. The idea began to bloom, strange and wonderful. She put the glasses on a coffee table in front of a sofa and sat on the sofa. 'Come over here, you odd little man,' she said. Mr Martin went over and sat beside her. It was difficult getting a cigarette out of the pack of Camels, but he managed it. She held a match for him, laughing. 'Well,' she said, handing him his drink, 'this is perfectly marvellous. You with a drink and a cigarette.'

Mr Martin puffed, not too awkwardly, and took a gulp of the highball. 'I drink and smoke all the time,' he said. He clinked his glass against hers. 'Here's nuts to that old windbag, Fitweiler,' he said, and gulped again. The stuff tasted awful, but he made no grimace. 'Really, Mr Martin,' she said, her voice and posture changing, 'you are insulting our employer.' Mrs Barrows was now all special adviser to the president. 'I am preparing a bomb,' said Mr Martin, 'which will blow the old goat higher than hell.' He had only had a little of the drink, which was not strong. It couldn't be that. 'Do you take dope or something?' Mrs Barrows asked coldly. 'Heroin,' said Mr Martin. 'I'll be coked to the gills when I bump that old buzzard off.' 'Mr Martin!' she shouted, getting to her feet. 'That will be all of that. You must go at once.' Mr Martin took another swallow of his drink. He tapped his cigarette out in the ashtray and put the pack of Camels on the coffee table. Then he got up. She stood glaring at him. He walked over and put on his hat and coat. 'Not a word about this,' he said, and laid an index finger against his lips. All Mrs Barrows could bring out was 'Really!' Mr Martin put his hand on the doorknob. 'I'm sitting in the catbird seat,' he said. He stuck his tongue out at her and left. Nobody saw him go.

Mr Martin got to his apartment, walking, well before eleven. No one saw him go in. He had two glasses of milk after brushing his teeth, and he felt elated. It wasn't tipsiness, because he hadn't been tipsy. Anyway, the walk had worn off all effects of the whisky. He got in bed and read a magazine for a while. He was asleep before midnight.

Mr Martin got to the office at eight-thirty the next morning, as usual. At a quarter to nine, Ulgine Barrows, who had never before arrived at work before ten, swept into his office. 'I'm reporting to Mr Fitweiler now!' she shouted. 'If he turns you over to the police, it's no more than you deserve!' Mr Martin gave her a look of shocked surprise. 'I beg your pardon?' he said. Mrs Barrows snorted and bounced out of the room, leaving Miss Paird and Joey Hart staring after her. 'What's the matter with that old devil now?' asked Miss Paird. 'I have no idea,' said Mr Martin, resuming his work. The other two looked at him and then at each other. Miss Paird got up and went out. She walked slowly past the closed door of Mr Fitweiler's office. Mrs Barrows was yelling inside, but she was not braying. Miss Paird could not hear what the woman was saying. She went back to her desk.

Forty-five minutes later, Mrs Barrows left the president's office and went into her own, shutting the door. It wasn't until half an hour later that Mr Fitweiler sent for Mr Martin. The head of the filing department, neat, quiet, attentive, stood in front of the old man's desk. Mr Fitweiler was pale and nervous. He took his glasses off and twiddled them. He made a small, bruffing sound in his throat. 'Martin,' he said, 'you have been with us more than twenty years.' 'Twenty-two sir,' said Mr Martin. 'In that time,' pursued the president, 'your work and your – uh – manner have been exemplary.' 'I trust so, sir,' said Mr. Martin. 'I have understood, Martin,' said Mr.Fitweiler, 'that you have never taken a drink or smoked.' 'That is correct, sir,' said Mr Martin. 'Ah, yes.' Mr Fitweiler polished his glasses. 'You may describe what you did after leaving the office yesterday, Martin,' he said. Mr Martin allowed less than a second for his bewildered pause. 'Certainly, sir,' he said. 'I walked home. Then I went to Schrafft's for dinner. Afterward I walked home again. I went to bed early, sir, and read a magazine for a while. I was asleep before eleven.' 'Ah, yes,' said Mr Fitweiler again. He was silent for a moment, searching for the proper words to say to the head of the filing department. 'Mrs Barrows,' he said finally, 'Mrs Barrows has worked hard, Martin very hard. It grieves me to report that she has suffered a severe breakdown. It has taken the form of a persecution complex accompanied by distressing hallucinations.' 'I am very sorry, sir,' said Mr Martin. 'Mrs Barrows is under the delusion,' continued Mr Fitweiler, 'that you visited her last evening and behaved yourself in an – uh – unseemly manner.' He raised his hand to silence Mr Martin's little pained outcry. 'It is the nature of these psychological diseases,' Mr Fitweiler said, 'to fix upon the least likely and most innocent party as the—uh—source of persecution. These matters are not for the lay mind to grasp, Martin. I've just had my psychiatrist, Dr Fitch, on the phone. He would not, of course, commit himself, but he made enough generalisations to substantiate my suspicions. I suggested to Mrs Barrows when she had completed her—uh—story to me this morning, that she visit Dr Fitch, for I suspected a condition at once. She flew, I regret to say, into a rage, and demanded—uh—requested that I call you on the carpet. You may not know, Martin, but Mrs Barrows had planned a reorganisation of you department – subject to my approval, of course, subject to my approval. This brought you, rather than anyone else, to her mind – but again that is a phenomenon for Dr Fitch and not for us. So, Martin, I am afraid Mrs Barrows' usefulness here is at an end.' 'I am dreadfully sorry, sir,' said Mr Martin.

It was at this point that the door to the office blew open with the suddenness of a gas-main explosion and Mrs Barrows catapulted through it. 'Is the little rat denying it?' she screamed. 'He can't get away with that!' Mr Martin got up and moved discreetly to a point beside Mr Firtweiler's chair. 'you drank and smoked at my apartment,' she bawled at Mr Martin, 'and you know it! You called Mr Fitweiler an old windbag and said you were going to blow him up when you got coked to the gills on your heroin!' She stopped yelling to catch her breath and a new glint came into her popping eyes. 'If you weren't such a drab, ordinary little man,' she said, 'I'd think you'd planned it all. Sticking your tongue out, saying you were sitting in the catbird seat, because you thought no one would believe me when I told it! My God, it's really too perfect!' She brayed loudly and hysterically, and the fury was on her again. She glared at Mr Fitweiler. 'Can't you see how he has tricked us, you old fool? Can't you see his little game?' But Mr Fitweiler had been surreptitiously pressing all the buttons under the top of his desk and employees of F & S began pouring into the room. 'Stockton,' said Mr Fitweiler, 'you and Fishbein will take Mrs Barrows to her home. Mrs Powell, you will go with them.' Stockton, who had played a little football in high school, blocked Mrs Barrows as she made for Mr Martin. It took him and Fishbein together to force her out of the door into the hall, crowded with stenographers and office boys. She was still screaming imprecations at Mr Martin, tangled and contradictory imprecations. The hubbub finally died out down the corridor.

'I regret that this has happened,' said Mr Fitweiler. 'I shall ask you to dismiss it from your mind, Martin.' 'Yes, sir,' said Mr Martin, anticipating his chief's 'That will be all' by moving to the door. 'I will dismiss it.' He went out and shut the door, and his step was light and quick in the hall. When he entered his department he had slowed down to his customary gait, and he walked quietly across the room to the W20 file, wearing a look of studious concentration.

The Cane in the Corridor

'Funny thing about post-operative mental states,' said Joe Fletcher, rocking the big brandy glass between the palms of his hands and studying the brown tides reflectively. 'They take all kinds of curious turns.'

George Minturn moved restlessly in his chair, making a new pattern of his long legs. 'Let's go to Barney's,' he said. 'Let's go to Barney's now.'

Mrs Minturn walked over and emptied an ashtray into the fireplace as eloquently as if she were winding the clock. 'It's much too late,' she said. 'I'm sure everybody we'd want to see has left there and gone home to bed.'

Minturn finished his brandy and poured out some more.

'You remember Reginald Gardiner's imitation of wallpaper,' continued Fletcher, 'in which he presented a visual design as making a pattern of sound? Many post-operative cases make those interesting transferences. I know one man who kept drawing on a piece of paper what the ringing of a telephone *looks* like.'

'I don't want to hear about him,' said Minturn.

Fletcher drank the last of his brandy and held up his glass; after a moment his host walked over and poured in a little more.

Mrs Minturn found herself finishing her own drink and getting another one, although she seldom touched anything after dinner. 'Here's to the Washington Bridge,' she said. 'Here's to some big dam or other. Let's talk about some big dam. After all, you're an engineer, Joe.'

Fletcher lighted a cigarette, holding his brandy glass between his knees. 'Which brings up an interesting point,' he said. 'I mean, if occupational experience gives a special shape and colour to the patient's perceptions, then the theory that it is not really a hallucination but a deeper insight into reality probably falls down. For instance, if the number eighteen clangs for one patient and whistles for another – say for George here – '

Minturn spilled ashes on the lapel of his dinner coat and rubbed them into it. 'I don't want to hear any numbers,' he said thickly. 'I don't want to hear any more about it.'

His wife, who had been trying to get Fletcher's eye but couldn't, since he continued to study his brandy, spoke up sharply. 'George is just getting over a frightful cold,' she said 'and he's prettily easily shaken. He would worry frightfully about people, but he doesn't dare think about them. They upset him so.' Fletcher did look at her now, and smiled. She realised she had not said what she had meant to say. Something oblique but cleverly phrased and nicely pointed had got lost on its way to her tongue. 'You think you're so darn smart,' she said.

Minturn got up and began to pace. The brandy had run out. He sat down and lighted a cigarette.

'Of course, the people that doctors refer to as squashes,' pursued Fletcher, 'the invertebrates, you might say, just lie there like vegetables. It is the high-strung cases that manifest the interesting – manifestations. As you just said, Nancy, you think you're so darn smart. I mean, hospitalisation moves the mind toward a false simplification. A man gets the idea that he can hold processes in his hand, the way I'm holding this glass. He lies there, you might say, pulling the easy little meanings out of life as simply as if they were daisy petals.'

'Daisy petals,' said Minturn. 'Where's brandy? Why isn't there any more brandy?'

'He gets the idea,' Fletcher went on, 'that he knows as much about life as Alfred North Whitehead or Carson McCullers.'

Minturn said, 'Oh, God.'

'Carson McCullers makes George nervous,' said Mrs Minturn, 'and you know it.'

'I ask you to remember I have scarcely seen you people since Carson McCullers began to write,' said Fletcher stiffly. 'I know 'Sanctuary' upset George so he had to go away to the mountains. I do know that.'

'He didn't go away to the mountains at all,' said Mrs Minturn. 'So you don't know that.'

'I want to go away to the mountains now,' said Minturn. He began pacing around again, picking up things.

'There's more brandy in the kitchen, darling,' said Mrs Minturn. 'In the kitchen,' she repeated as he started upstairs.

'Oh,' said Minturn. He went out to the kitchen.

Mrs Minturn went over to Fletcher and stood looking down at him. 'It's very sweet of you, Joe, to keep harping on hospitals and sick people and mental states,' she said. 'I know why you're doing it. You're doing it because George didn't come to see you when you were in the hospital. You know very well that George is too sensitive to visit people in the hospital.'

Fletcher stood up, too. 'Is that why *you* didn't come to see me?' he asked. She was taller than he was. He sat down again.

'Yes, it was, if you want to know so much,' she said. 'George would have sensed it and he would have worried about you all the time. As it was, he *did* worry about you all the time. But he can't stand things the way you can. You know how sensitive he's always been.'

Fletcher tried to drink out of his empty glass. 'He wasn't so goddam sensitive when we were both with the Cleveland Telephone Company. He wasn't so goddam sensitive then. No, he was practically a regular guy.'

Mrs Minturn drew herself up a little higher. 'It is just quite possible, perhaps,' she said, 'that you were just not quite perceptious at that time.' She went slowly back to her chair and sat down as Minturn came in with a bottle of brandy and a corkscrew.

'Here,' he said, handing them to Fletcher. Fletcher put down his glass, inserted the corkscrew into the centre of the cork, twisted it competently, and pulled out the cork. 'Wonderful thing, technology,' said Minturn, 'wonderful thing, wonderful thing. I want a drink.' Fletcher poured a great splash of brandy into his host's glass and another into his own.

'He doesn't happen to mean he *believes* in it,' said Mrs Minturn. 'The trouble with you is you can't tell when a person is allusive even.'

'You're thinking of Technocracy,' Fletcher told her, taking her glass and pouring a small quantity of brandy into it with studious precision.

'Maybe,' said Mrs Minturn, darkly, 'and just maybe not.'

'Why can't we go home now? Why can't we go home now, Nancy?' said Minturn from deep down in his chair.

'We *are* home, dear,' said Mrs Minturn. She turned to Fletcher. 'Anybody that thinks I can't appreciate a game that two can play at is definitely,' said Mrs Minturn, hiccuping, 'crazy.' She held her breath and tried counting ten slowly.

'Why don't you try bending over and drinking out of the opposite side of your glass?' asked Fletcher.

Minturn sat up a little in his chair.

'Don't have to say things like that,' he said, severely.

To compensate for her hiccups, Mrs Minturn assumed a posture of strained dignity. Minturn slid farther down into his chair. They both watched Fletcher, who had set the brandy revolving in his glass and was studying it. He took a sip of his drink. 'It is a common misconception,' he said, 'that post-operative mental states disappear on the patient's advent from the hospital. Out of the hospital, they might recur at any time, and some pretty strange phenomena could happen – as in the case of the hospitalisation of a friend.'

'If you're just trying to get George down, it's not going to be of the least consequence. I can assure you of that,' said Mrs Minturn. 'He's stronger than you are in lots of more important ways.'

'Phenomena,' said Minturn.

'I'm talking of what *I* might do, not of what George might do,' said Fletcher, 'in case you consider the manifestation what you choose to call weakness.'

'Well,' said Mrs Minturn, 'I certainly do – that and meanness.'

'I want to see Mrs Trimingham,' said Minturn. 'I want to go to Bermuda.'

'I suppose it would be too much to say that you can't very well disprove what I'm saying till I say it,' said Fletcher.

'No, it wouldn't,' said Mrs Minturn. 'I don't see why we can't talk about the Grand Coolidge Dam, or something.' She laughed. 'That's really frightfully funny. It really is.' She laughed again.

Minturn had closed his eyes, but he opened them again. 'Can't say I do,' he said. 'Can't say I do.'

Fletcher went over and splashed some more brandy into Minturn's glass. 'Let us say that George is lying in the hospital,' he said. 'Now, because of a recurring phenomena, I call on him every day.'

'That's cheap' said Mrs Minturn, 'and that's pompous.'

'It's no more pompous than it is predictable,' said Fletcher, sharply. 'It's a condition. It just so happens that it might take the turn of me calling on George every day, from the time he goes in until he gets out.'

'You can't do that,' said George. 'There's such a thing as the law.'

'Of course he can't,' said Mrs Minturn. 'Besides, George is not going to the hospital.'

'I'm not going to the hospital,' said Minturn.

'Everybody goes to the hospital sooner or later,' said Fletcher. His voice was rising.

'Nine hundred million people don't,' said Mrs Minturn, 'all the time.'

'I'm stating a pathological case!' shouted Fletcher. 'Hypotheti-
cal. George has been lying there in that bed for six weeks!'

'No,' said Minturn.

'You ought to be ashamed of yourself,' said Mrs Minturn.

'Why?' asked Fletcher. 'I'm not saying there is anything the
matter with him. He's convalescing, but he can't get up.'

'Why can't I get up?' asked Minturn.

'Because you're too weak. You have no more strength than a
house mouse. You feel as if you were coming apart like a cheap
croquet mallet. If you tried to stand, your knees would bend the
wrong way, like a flamingo's.'

'I want to go home,' mumbled Minturn.

'You *are* home,' said his wife.

'He means from the hospital,' Fletcher told her, 'in the corridors
of which, by the way, you hear my cane tapping practically all the
time.'

'What are *you* doing there?' said Minturn thickly.

'I come to see you every day,' said Fletcher. 'I have been to see
you every day since you got there.' He had been moving around
the room, and now he went back and sat down.

'Can't stand you calling on me every day,' said Minturn. He
finished his drink and poured a new one with some effort.

'Don't worry about it, George,' said Mrs Minturn. 'We'll take
you to the Mayo brothers or someplace and he'll never find out
about it.'

'I don't want to go to the Mayo brothers,' said Minturn.

Fletcher sat forward in his chair. 'And what's more,' he said, 'I
bring you very strange things. That's part of it. That's part of the
phenomena. I bring you puzzles that won't work, linked nails that
won't come apart, pigs in clover in which the little balls are glued
to the bottom of the box. I bring you mystery novels in Yiddish, and
artificial flowers made of wire and beads, and horehound candy.'

'Terrible, terrible rat,' said Mrs Minturn, 'terrible rat Fletcher.'

'Police find something to do about that,' said Minturn. 'Such a
thing as law and order. Such a thing as malpractice.'

'And licorice whips,' continued Fletcher, 'and the complete
files of *Physical Culture* for 1931; and matchboxes that go broo-
oo-oo, broo-oo-oo.'

'Broo,' said Minturn. 'I want to go to Twenty-One.'

'Terrible, terrible, terrible rat,' said Mrs Minturn.

'I see,' said Fletcher. 'You don't even feel sorry for poor old
tap-tap. Tap, tap, tap, tap, tap.'

'What's that?' said Minturn.

'That's my cane in the corridor,' said Fletcher. 'You are lying there, trying to unwrassle something I have brought you, when, tap, tap, tap, here I come again.'

'Terrible rat, go home,' said Mrs Minturn.

Fletcher bowed to her gravely. 'I'm going,' he said. 'It constitutes the first occasion on which I have ever been ejected from this or any other house, but that is as it should be, I presume.'

'Don't throw anybody out,' said Minturn. 'Tap, tap, tap,' he added.

Halfway to the hall door, Fletcher turned. 'That's right, laugh,' he said. 'Tap, tap, tap, tap, tap, then.'

'Tap, tap, tap,' said Minturn from far down near the floor. A new attack of hiccups kept Mrs Minturn speechless, but she stood up as her guest went out into the hall. Minturn was still saying 'Tap, tap,' and Mrs Minturn was hiccuping, as Fletcher found his hat and coat and went out the front door into the melting snow, looking for a taxi.

The Princess and the Tin Box

Once upon a time, in a far country, there lived a king whose daughter was the prettiest princess in the world. Her eyes were like the cornflower, her hair was sweeter than the hyacinth, and her throat made the swan look dusty.

From the time she was a year old, the princess had been showered with presents. Her nursery looked like Cartier's window. Her toys were all made of gold or platinum or diamonds or emeralds. She was not permitted to have wooden blocks or china dolls or rubber dogs or linen books, because such materials were considered cheap for the daughter of a king.

When she was seven, she was allowed to attend the wedding of her brother and throw real pearls at the bride instead of rice. Only the nightingale, with his lyre of gold, was permitted to sing for the princess. The common blackbird, with his boxwood flute, was kept out of the palace grounds. She walked in silver-and-samite slippers to a sapphire-and-topaz bathroom and slept in an ivory bed inlaid with rubies.

On the day the princess was eighteen, the king sent a royal ambassador to the courts of five neighbouring kingdoms to announce that he would give his daughter's hand in marriage to the prince who brought her the gift she liked the most.

The first prince to arrive at the palace rode a swift white stallion and laid at the feet of the princess an enormous apple made of solid gold which he had taken from a dragon who had guarded it for a thousand years. It was placed on a long ebony table set up to hold the gifts of the princess's suitors. The second prince, who came on a grey charger, brought her a nightingale made of a thousand diamonds, and it was placed beside the golden apple. The third prince, riding on a black horse, carried a great jewel box made of platinum and sapphires, and it was placed next to the diamond nightingale. The fourth prince, astride a fiery yellow horse, gave the princess a gigantic heart made of rubies and pierced by an emerald arrow. It was placed next to the platinum-and-sapphire jewel box.

Now the fifth prince was the strongest and handsomest of all the five suitors, but he was the son of a poor king whose realm had been overrun by mice and locusts and wizards and mining engineers so that there was nothing much of value left in it. He came plodding up to the palace of the princess on a plough horse and he brought her a small tin box filled with mica and feldspar and hornblende which he had picked up on the way.

The other princes roared with disdainful laughter when they saw the tawdry gift the fifth prince had brought to the princess. But she examined it with great interest and squealed with delight, for all her life she had been glutted with precious stones and priceless metals, but she had never seen tin before or mica or feldspar or hornblende. The tin box was placed next the the ruby heart pierced with an emerald arrow.

'Now,' the king said to his daughter, 'you must select the gift you like best and marry the prince that brought it.'

The princess smiled and walked up to the table and picked up the present she liked the most. It was the platinum-and-sapphire jewel box, the gift of the third prince.

'The way I figure it,' she said, 'is this. It is a very large and expensive box, and when I am married, I will meet many admirers who will give me precious gems with which to fill it to the top. Therefore, it is the most valuable of all the gifts my suitors have brought me and I like it the best.'

The princess married the third prince that very day in the midst of great merriment and high revelry. More than a hundred thousand pearls were thrown at her and she loved it.

Moral: All those who thought the princess was going to select the tin box filled with worthless stones instead of one of the other gifts will kindly stay after class and write one hundred times on the blackboard 'I would rather have a hunk of aluminium silicate than a diamond necklace.'

The Waters of the Moon

I had broken away from an undulant discussion of kinetic dimensionalism and was having a relaxed moment with a slender woman I had not seen before, who described herself as a chaoticist, when my hostess, an avid disturber of natural balances and angles of repose, dragged me off to meet the guest of honour, a Mr Peifer, editor of a literary review. 'Holds his liquor beautifully,' my hostess said. 'Burns it up, I guess. He's terribly intense.' Peifer was pacing back and forth on a rug, haranguing a trapped etcher whose reluctant eyes kept following him as if he were a tennis rally.

'No, I'm not interested in the ageing American *female* author,' Peifer was saying. 'That's a phenomenon that confounds analysis. The female writer's fertility of invention and glibness of style usually survive into senility, just as her artistic gestation frequenlty seems to be independent of the nourishment of thought.'

Peifer made three turns of the rug in silence. He had the expression of a chemist absorbed in abstruse formulae. 'I am interested in the male American writer who peters out in his fifties, who has the occupational span of a hockey player. The tempo of our American life may have something to do with it, but there must be a dozen other factors that dry up the flow of ideas and transform a competent prose style into the meagre iterations of a train announcer.'

My hostess finally broke in, and Peifer stopped pacing to shake hands. The etcher seized the opportunity to disappear. 'Mr Thurber is fifty-three,' my hostess said. 'He hasn't written anything since last April.' Peifer looked at me as if I were the precipitate of a moderately successful test-tube experiment. My first name suddenly reminded him of a tangent of his theme. 'Take Henry James,' he said. 'If he had lived in this country, he would probably have spent his middle years raising collies or throwing darts. It is preposterous to assume, however, that region or climate is the important factor. There must be something, though, in the American way of life and habit of thought. I want to get Wylie or De Voto or somebody to do a comprehensive treatise on the subject, looking at it from the viewpoints of marriage, extramarital relations, the educational system, home environment, the failure of religion, the tyranny of money, and the rich breeding ground of decomposition which I believe is to be found in syphilophobia, prostatitis, early baldness, peptic ulcer, edentulous cases, true and hysterical impotence, and spreading of the metatarsals.' I tried to wrench a tray of Martinis from a man in a white coat, but he would only let me have one. 'Let's go over and sit down on that sofa,' Peifer said. I followed him, glancing ruefully over my shoulder at my lost chaoticist. 'It's a difficult article,' I said. 'If you use names, it's dangerous, and if you don't, it won't be interesting. You can't very well say that Joseph Doakes, after petering out on page 73 of his unfinished novel, "Whatever gods", a childlike and feathery permutation of his first book, "Fear Set Free", is living in sin with his cook and spends his time cutting the pips out of playing cards.'

Peifer took my olive. 'The article is not to be a gossip column,' he said. 'It's to be a scholarly treatise. I am interested in exploring the causes of literary collapse, not in collecting scandalous post-disintegration case histories of quixotic individuals who would no doubt have gone to pieces in precisely the same way had they been milliners or pharmacists' mates.'

'Then, unhappily,' I said, 'you cannot follow the old codgers past the hour of their deterioration, and in so doing you will omit a great deal of fascinating sequelae. You are interested only in causation. You would trace the career of, let us say, Bruce Balliol up to that afternoon in June when he abruptly began to write the middle section of "Love Not the Wind" in the manner of the late Senator Albert J. Beveridge, and realized to his dismay that he was washed up at fifty-six. I would take him through his divorce, his elopement with the hairdresser, and those final baffling years on the peacock ranch.'

A grim man I had never seen before walked up to us, dribbling his Manhattan. 'Cora in the bells and grass,' he said. 'Cora with a cherry halfway to her lips.' The man walked away. 'I like Eve better than Cora,' I said. Peifer apparently didn't know the poem the man had paraphrased. 'You do?' he said, with his laboratory glint. 'You were talking,' I said. 'Go on.' Peifer took a curved briar pipe out of his pocket and rubbed the bowl on his pants leg. He began to chew on the stem of his pipe.

'That was poor old Greg Selby,' I said, 'a perfect specimen for your analysis. He stopped writing suddenly, a fortnight after his fifty-fourth birthday. Bang!' Peifer started. 'Like that,' I said. 'His felicity of style was the envy and despair of us all, and then abruptly one day he began to write like a doorman cockeyed on cooking sherry.' 'I never heard of any writer named Greg Selby,' Peifer said. I lifted a Martini from a passing tray. 'He has never published anything,' I said. 'He is going to leave all his work to Harvard, to be published a thousand years from now. Greg's writing has what he calls Projected Meaning. He feels that in another millennium the intellectuals will understand it readily enough. I have never made head or tail of any of his stuff myself, but there is no missing the unique quality of the most exquisite English prose of our time.'

Peifer made figure eights in the air with his pipe. 'He seems a little special,' he said. 'I'm not interested in idiosyncratic variables, except, perhaps, as footnotes.'

'He is a male American writer who petered out in his middle fifties,' I insisted. 'He fits in perfectly.'

'What I have in mind is the published writer of established merit,' my companion said as I stopped another Martini tray, 'but go on. What happened to this man Selby?'

'His first wife, Cora,' I began, 'claimed to have discovered that his last book, "Filiring Gree," was his next-to-last book, "Saint Tomany's Rain," written backward. It was insupportable to Greg that his wife should go through his books like a public accountant investigating a bank ledger. He threw her and her Siamese cats out of the house – the macaw wouldn't go. He had not heard the last of her, however. She called him up every few days and in the falsetto of a little child asked him why he didn't dramatise the Little Colonel stories for Margaret O'Brien. She divorced him, finally, and married a minor-league outfielder.'

'This is really terribly special,' Peifer complained, signalling a tray of highballs.

'Cora was ordinary enough. It was Eve who was special. She was the author of a number of mystery books. You probably remember "Pussy Wants a Coroner."' Peifer replied, a little pettishly, that he did not read mysteries.

'After her marriage to Greg,' I went on, 'Eve's books took on a curiously Gothic tone; the style was cold and blocky, and the plots had all the flexibility of an incantation. She explained to her alarmed publishers that she was trying to write for the understanding of intellectuals a thousand years ago.' Peifer put his drink on the floor and stood up. 'I presume you would consider Douglas Bryce a published author of established merit, wouldn't you?' I demanded. I had thought the name up fast. 'Well,' Peifer said uneasily. He sat down again.

'Doug,' I said, 'ran out of ideas and his command of sentence construction at the same time, on a Wednesday. He was fifty-eight. That was a long time ago. He died in 1932, on his chinchilla farm, and only the hatcheck girl, Dolores, was at his bedside. Nell left him after the Lawrence Stone incident.'

Piefer recrossed his legs restlessly and reached for another highball. 'It would be as hard to find a copy of "The Tenant of the Room" now as it would be to turn up a first edition of "V.V.'s Eyes",' I told him. '"The Tenant" was Doug's last book. It was a flimsy rehash of his earlier "A Piece in Bloom". The love story was a little more disgusting, but in general it was a slight rearrangement of the well-worn characters and incidents. Doug had once had a facile and effective style, but the writing in "The Tenant" fell well within the capabilities of a shrewd pin boy.'

I took another Martini. 'Get on with it,' Peifer said.

'Nell once told me that after the failure of "The Tenant", Doug spent his days making cryptic and vainglorious notes on pieces of Kleenex, doorjambs, the flyleaves of books, and shirt fronts. He would jot down such things as "Translate Lippmann into Latin", "Reply to Shelburne Essays", "Refute Toynbee", "Collaborate with G.B.S.?", "Call Gilbert Miller". Other notes indicated that he planned a history of the New York, New Haven & Hartford in verse, an account of women in sports, to be called "Atlanta to Babe Didrikson", and a pageant based on the Tristram legends, in which he proposed to star the late Devereux Milburn.'

'I really must go,' Peifer said. He stood up and then resumed his seat. 'What was the Lawrence Stone incident?' he asked.

'Just before he bought the chinchilla farm, Nell found, scribbled on the bathroom wall, "The Shore; The Plain; The Mountain, a trilogy by Douglas Bryce". Under that he had written "A monumental achievement", which he had signed "Van Wyck Brooks". But he was onto himself at last; he was tired and he was through and he knew it. The reservoir of his natural talent had run dry and he had been reaching for the waters of the moon. But as I say, he was onto himself. Under it all he had scrawled, almost illegibly, "a trilogy wilogy by Brycey-Wycey".'

'Who was this man Stone? And then I must go,' Peifer said. 'People are beginning to sing.'

'Doug had one more project,' I said. 'He conceived the idea of writing a long biography of a man picked at random in the street. The book was to be called "Let Twenty Pass". He stood one day at the corner of Fifth Avenue and Forty-fourth Street, counted off twenty men who walked by going north, and accosted the twenty-first. The twenty-first was a large, preoccupied mining engineer named Lawrence Stone. He called the police and a rather nasty fuss was kicked up in the papers. It came out, you remember, that Stone was quite deaf, and his functional disability had twisted Doug's proposal into a shockingly complex plan to seize the major networks. Dolores was passing when Doug accosted Stone, and her testimony as to what was actually said cleared Bryce. It was a near thing, though.'

Peifer twisted around on the sofa, slowly and with difficulty, as if invisible blankets hampered his legs. I saw that his unfriendly stare glittered frostily in almost imperceptibly crossed eyes. I wondered I had not noticed before that his liquor, much of it unburned, had left him, in spite of a fluent grasp on his subject, balanced precariously between command and dissolution. His expression took away all my pride of invention in the garish show of figures I had conjured up to ornament his theme. I had been careless, too, in the name of the mining engineer, and Peifer had caught me out. 'I happen to be familiar with Browning,' he said with shrewd dignity, 'and I happen to know how the line that begins "Let twenty pass" ends.'

I was conscious of a figure at my shoulder. Someone had come to save me. It was the slender lady, my dark lady of chaos, grown a little mistier with the passing of the afternoon and possessed now of the posture of the rose in a summer wind. I stood up, and Peifer managed it, too. 'Nell,' I said, 'may I present Mr Peifer?' He bowed stiffly. 'This is Nell Bryce,' I told him. The game was up, but here I was, kicking field goals by moonlight. 'Piefer here,' I said, 'would not have followed Bierce beyond the Rio Grande or Villon through the porte of St Denis to see in what caprice or rondeaux their days came to an end.'

'Let's phone the police and plague 'em till hell won't have it,' the lady said. It seemed to hurt Peifer like a slap. He bowed, almost too low to sustain the moral advantage he undoubtedly held over both of us. 'It is a great pity, Madam,' he said, tightly, 'that you mythical husband had the misfortune to encounter an engineer named Stone. Ah, what a flaw in the verisilimitude was there! It is a great pity your husband did not have the luck to encounter an engineer named Costello or McKelway or Shapiro.' The dark lady listened to him with the expression of one who is receiving complicated directions in a great, strange town.

Peifer turned a cold, uncertain eye on me. 'Let twenty pass,' he

snarled, 'and stone the twenty-first.' The dark lady watched him,
on a quick opening play, break between guard and centre of a
mixed quartet. 'Now, how in the God's name' – she had a charm-
.ing diaphragmatic convulsion – 'did he know my husband was
mythical?' It was too long a story to go into. I took her arm and, in
silence led her to the telephone to call the police.

The Lady on the Bookcase

One day twelve years ago an outraged cartoonist, four of whose drawings had been rejected in a clump by *The New Yorker*, stormed into the office of Harold Ross, editor of the magazine. 'Why is it,' demanded the cartoonist, 'that you reject my work and publish drawings by a fifth-rate artist like Thurber?' Ross came quickly to my defence like the true friend and devoted employer he is. 'You mean third-rate,' he said quietly, but there was a warning glint in his steady grey eyes that caused the discomfited cartoonist to beat a hasty retreat.

With the exception of Ross, the interest of editors in what I draw has been rather more journalistic than critical. They want to know if it is true that I draw by moonlight, or under water, and when I say no, they lose interest until they hear the rumour that I found the drawings in an old trunk or that I do the captions while my nephew makes the sketches.

The other day I was shoving some of my originals around on the floor (I do not draw on the floor; I was just shoving the originals around) and they fell, or perhaps I pushed them, into five separate and indistinct categories. I have never wanted to write about my drawings, and I still don't want to, but it occurred to me that it might be a good idea to do it now, when everybody is busy with something else, and get it over quietly.

Category No. 1, then, which may be called the Unconscious or Stream of Nervousness category, is represented by 'With you I have known peace, Lida, and now you say you're going crazy' and the drawing entitled with simple dignity, 'Home'. These drawings were done while the artist was thinking of something else (or so he has been assured by experts) and hence his hand was guided by the Unconscious which, in turn, was more or less influenced by the Subconscious.

Students of Jung have instructed me that Lida and the House-Woman are representations of the *anima*, the female essence or directive which floats around in the ageless universal Subconscious of Man like a tadpole in a cistern. Less intellectual critics insist that the two ladies are actual persons I have consciously known. Between these two schools of thought lies a discourag-

'With you I have known peace, Lida, and now you say you're going crazy.'

Home

ingly large space of time extending roughly from 1,000,000 B.C. to the middle Nineteen Thirties.

Whenever I try to trace the true identity of the House-Woman, I get to thinking of Mr Jones. He appeared in my office one day twelve years ago, said he was Mr Jones, and asked me to lend him 'Home' for reproduction in an art magazine. I never saw the drawing again. Tall, well-dressed, kind of sad-looking chap, and as well spoken a gentleman as you would want to meet.

Category No. 2 brings us to Freud and another one of those discouragingly large spaces – namely, the space between the Concept of the Purely Accidental and the theory of Haphazard Determination. Whether chance is capricious or we are all prisoners of pattern is too long and cloudy a subject to go into here. I shall consider each of the drawings in Category No. 2, explaining what happened and leaving the definition of the forces involved up to you. The seal on top of the bed, then ('All right, have it your way – you heard a seal bark'), started out to be a seal on a rock. The rock, in the process of being drawn, began to look like the

'All right, have it your way – you heard a seal bark.'

'That's my first wife up there, and this is the present
Mrs Harris.'

head of a bed, so I made a bed out of it, put a man and wife in the
bed, and stumbled onto the caption as easily and unexpectedly as
the seal had stumbled into the bedroom.

The woman on top of the bookcase ('That's my first wife up
there, and this is the *present* Mrs Harris') was originally designed to
be a woman crouched on the top step of a staircase, but since the
tricks and conventions of perspective and planes sometimes fail
me, the staircase assumed the shape of a bookcase and was
finished as such, to the surprise and embarrassment of the first Mrs
Harris, the present Mrs Harris, the lady visitor, Mr Harris and me.
Before *The New Yorker* would print the drawing, they phoned me
long distance to inquire whether the first Mrs Harris was alive or
dead or stuffed. I replied that my taxidermist had advised me that
you cannot stuff a woman, and that my physician had informed
me that a dead lady cannot support herself on all fours. This
meant, I said, that the first Mrs Harris was unquestionably alive.

The man riding on the other man's shoulders in the bar ('For the
last time, you and your horsie get away from me and stay away!')
was intended to be standing alongside the irate speaker, but I

*'For the last time, you and your horsie get away from me
and stay away!'*

started his head up too high and made it too small, so that he
would have been nine feet tall if I had completed his body that
way. It was but the work of thirty-two seconds to put him on
another man's shoulders. As simple or, if you like, as complicated
as that. The psychological factors which may be present here are,
as I have indicated, elaborate and confused. Personally, I like Dr
Claude Thornway's theory of the Deliberate Accident or Con-
ditioned Mistake.

Category No. 3 is perhaps a variant of Category No. 2; indeed,
they may even be identical. The dogs in 'The father belonged to
some people who were driving through in a Packard' were drawn
as a captionless spot, and the interior with figures just sort of grew
up around them. The hippopotamus in 'What have you done with
Dr Millmoss?' was drawn to amuse my small daughter. Something
about the creature's expression when he was completed convinced me that he had recently eaten a man. I added the hat and

'The father belonged to some people who were driving through in a Packard.'

'What have you done with Dr Millmoss?'

pipe and Mrs Millmoss, and the caption followed easily enough.
Incidentally, my daughter, who was 2 years old at the time,
identified the beast immediately. 'That's a hippotomanus,' she
said. *The New Yorker* was not so smart. They described the
drawing for their files as follows: 'Woman with strange animal.'
The New Yorker was nine years old at the time.

Category No. 4 is represented by perhaps the best known of
some fifteen drawings belonging to this special grouping, which
may be called the Contributed Idea Category. This drawing
('Touché!') was originally done for *The New Yorker* by Carl Rose,
caption and all. Mr Rose is a realistic artist, and his gory scene
distressed the editors, who hate violence. They asked Rose if he
would let me have the idea since there is obviously no blood to
speak of in the people I draw. Rose graciously consented. No one
who looks at 'Touché!' believes that the man whose head is in the
air is really dead. His opponent will hand it back to him with
profuse apologies, and the discommoded fencer will replace it on
his shoulders and say, 'No harm done, forget it.' Thus the old
controversy as to whether death can be made funny is left just

'Touché!'

'Well, I'm disenchanted too. We're all disenchanted.'

'You said a moment ago that everybody you look at seems to be
a rabbit. Now just what do you mean by that, Mrs Sprague?'

where it was before Carl Rose came along with his wonderful idea.

Category No. 5, our final one, can be called, believe it or not, the Intentional or Thought-Up Category. The idea for each of these two drawings just came to me and I sat down and made a sketch to fit the prepared caption. Perhaps, in the case of 'Well, I'm disenchanted, too. We're all disenchanted,' another one of those Outside Forces played a part. That is, I may have overheard a husband say to his wife, on the street or at a party, 'I'm disenchanted.' I do not think this is true, however, in the case of the rabbit-headed doctor and his woman patient. I believe that scene and its caption came to me one night in bed. I may have got the idea in a doctor's office or a rabbit hutch, but I don't think so.

If you want to, you can cut these drawings out and push them around on the floor, making your own categories or applying your own psychological theories; or you can even invent some fresh rumours. I should think it would be more fun, though, to take a nap, or baste a roast, or run around the reservoir in Central Park.

Here Come the Tigers

It was after midnight and I had got up to turn off the radio and go to bed when a baritone began to sing 'Bye-Bye, Blackbird' with the rueful reverence the song deserves. I sat down again, and I was lost. If I had shut off the radio, turned out the lights, and locked the door, Jordan and Hayes would have driven up to a dark house and gone away, or if they had hammered on the door, I would have let them hammer till they got discouraged and drove off. The lights were on, though, and the door was unlocked. The tyres of a car swashed over the gravel of the driveway and came to a sudden, complaining stop. My door opened and they tumbled in without knocking, like a pair of comics taking an encore. I turned off the radio and reached for the light switch.

'Hold!' Jordan cried. 'Stay that naughty hand!'

I took my hand off the switch. 'I'm tired,' I said, 'and Alice is asleep.'

'Sleep! Sleep – on a night of wild discovery!' Jordan moaned. He went over to the bar in a corner of the living room and began mixing a bourbon-and-soda. Hayes took Jordan's place at the bar when his companion flopped into a chair and swung one leg over an arm. 'We have discovered a new dimension of meaning,' Jordan said. He took a great gulp of his drink. 'And a new plane of beauty.'

'You want a drink?' Hayes asked me.

'It's late,' I said, 'and I'm tired.'

Jordan snorted, choked on his whisky, and coughed for a full minute. 'The man wants torpor,' he spluttered finally. 'On a night like this, the man wants torpor.'

'Torpor is a good word,' Hayes said. He sat on the arm of a chair. 'Shall we take it apart for him?'

'You guys are stiff,' I said.

Jordan frowned, finished his drink, and went back to the bar. 'Stiff is better,' he said. 'I think stiff is probably perfect. Let me get at it.' He dropped into the chair again, with a new highball.

I stared at the ceiling. If I didn't humour them, they might go away.

'We're starting too high,' Jordan said. 'We're the hell too high. He won't get it. Look at him.'

'Nuts,' I said coldly.

'Let me unwrap stiff for you,' Jordan said. 'God knows that ought to be simple enough. Listen to this. It's perfect. Stiff, tiff, fists, fits.'

'He means that the mood and tone and colour of a word are echoed in its component parts,' Hayes said. 'Tiff is argument, fist is fight, fits—fits—'

'Don't make it glare,' Jordan said. 'You're making it glare. Let him feel it. You got to feel it.'

'Look—' I began wanly.

Jordan regarded me sorrowfully and shook his head. 'He's going to compare it to Joyce or Dada or Gertrude Stein,' he said. 'He is an enemy of the new dimension. Oh, no, he can't be,' he added. 'Not in *this* house he can't be.' He had some trouble getting up, but he made the bar.

'It's *his* house,' Hayes said.

I was glad he was soberer than Jordan, who after a moment of deep thought said, 'Last place in the world a man should make an ass of himself. Host, you know, and all that.'

'Where have you guys been?' I asked.

Jordan looked at Hayes and shrugged, splashing a dollop of his new drink on the carpet. 'We have been in a new dimension of meaning and beauty,' he said, 'but I doubt if you could understand it.'

'Well, what the hell is it?' I demanded. I went to the bar and poured myself a short drink. 'Are you going to crawl around it all night, or are you coming out with it?'

'Tell him the quatrain,' Jordan said. 'I want him to hear the quatrain.'

Hayes studied the floor for a while. Then he recited the quatrain:

> 'There are lips in pistol
> And mist in times,
> Cats in crystal,
> And mice in chimes.'

I stared coldly at Jordan's transfigured face. 'Is this the spearhead of the New Beauty?' I asked.

Jordan globbered his drink down, ran his hand through his hair, and glared at me demoniacally. 'Shows what What's-his-name of

''Christabel'' and Keats of ''Eve of St Agnes'' could have done if the goddam fairy casements had opened on this lovely dimension!' he shouted.

'Coleridge,' Hayes said. He was nursing his drink along, and seemed to be getting sober.

Jordan went to the bar and sloshed out more bourbon. 'Well?' he demanded, but he didn't wait for me to answer. 'We were unlocking animals from almost every word you can think of when we got to cats in crystal and mice in chimes. Tell him some of 'em, Tom. You got 'em all written down.'

Hayes put his drink on the floor and pulled a piece of folded cardboard out of his pocket. I saw that it was a dinner menu with pencil scribblings on the back. 'There's the wolf in flower, the gander in danger, and the frog in forget,' he said. 'There's the emu in summer, the ant in autumn, the wren in winter, and the pig in spring.' He turned the cardboard upside down and scowled at it. 'There's the gnu in jungle,' he went on, 'the swan in answer, and the toad in toward.' He put the menu down, and I thought he looked a little unhappy, as if the whisky and the spell of the new dimension were wearing off at the same time.

Jordan kept snapping his fingers, trying to remember other beasts in other words.

'Try to find the tiger in a six-letter word,' Hayes said to me. 'It isn't easy. There are three six-letter words with tiger, but it isn't easy.'

'It's not a game, it's more than a game,' Jordan said severely. 'Let's not get back to the game.'

'It began as a game,' Hayes said to me. 'It's an old word game. You try to see how many words you can make out of another word.'

'We played it a million times before,' Jordan said, 'but tonight, for the first time, I see what we got, like Emily What's-her-name hearing the river in the trees. You might hear the wind in the trees all your life and never hear the river. Give me that thing, Tom.' He reached out and took the menu from Hayes, and began turning it slowly in his big hands. The writing on the back apparently ran in all directions. He sighed dolefully and handed it back to Hayes. 'There's practically a sentence in woman,' he said. 'It's perfect. See if you can find the sentence, Tom.'

Hayes patted away an incipient yawn. 'Woman: moan now won wan man,' he chanted, and then the yawn got the best of him.

'What'd I say it had in it, Tom?'

Hayes consulted the back of the menu. 'The thunder of Genesis,' he announced finally, 'it says here.'

'It's practically Biblical,' Jordan said, 'with only five letters.' He went to the bar again. 'Who wants a drink?' he asked. Neither of us said anything. Hayes had slumped a little in his chair. I leaned back, gazed at the ceiling, and hunted the tiger. For the next five minutes, I heard the sound of Jordan's voice but I didn't take in the sense. I found the roach in orchard, the horse in shore, the owl in wobble, the stag in ghastly, and the bear and zebra in brazen, but no glimmer of a tiger anywhere.

'It's like little boxes, one inside each other,' Jordan was saying when I came out of my own jungle of words. 'You lift out concentric meanings of practically identical mood and tone. Yet people have let the component parts of words go for a thousand years. They lose the depth and the roundness and the whole quality.' He turned to Hayes. 'Take pistol apart for Jim,' he begged. 'Take pistol apart.' I got up and went to the bar and poured out a stiff rye. 'Go ahead,' I said.

'It kind of rips and squirts and goes all to hell, the way pistol should,' Jordan said by way of foreword.

'Shoot,' I said.

'No gags,' Jordan implored me. 'For God sake, no gags.'

'Pistol,' Hayes began. 'Slip, spit, split, spilt, spoil, spoilt, slop, slot, tips, tops, spot, pots, stop.'

'You see what I mean?' Jordan asked. I visualised the word and studied it for a while.

'He left out oils and soil,' I said finally, 'and what are Lois and silo doing in pistol?'

Jordan turned to Hayes, who had shut his eyes. 'Didn't I tell you we'd be up against that?' he demanded. 'What'd I say we'd be up against, Tom?'

'The obscurantism of the explicit,' Hayes brought out after frowning over it.

'That's it! That's what I said we'd be up against, like in chalice.'

Hayes decided to try another drink, and he went over and poured himself a short one. 'You get lace and hail and ice and Alice in chalice,' he said, 'but you got lice to account for.'

'So what?' said Jordan. 'So what the hell?' He spread his hands.

'What about the rats in crystal, with the cats?' I asked.

'Jordan hasn't got the technic and ethic worked out yet,' Hayes told me.

'I can handle the rats,' Jordan said.

'And the salt and the slat and the cyst and the cart?' I asked.

'Yeh, and the star and the cry and the satyr. They all mix into crystal.'

Hayes yawned openly. He was drinking slowly. 'It seems a little thin, somehow,' he said. 'I mean the whole thing, in times like these.'

'What does?' Jordan stared at him blankly.

I saved an argument by suddenly running across Roget in forget. 'If there were no forget,' I said to Jordan, 'it would not be necessary to create Roget.'

'I don't think you get the idea,' he said. 'I don't think he gets the idea, Tom. What was it I said earlier this evening? I said, "Tom, he'll never get it in a million years." I said, "Tom, the obscurantism of the explicit is what's going to louse up this lovely thing." Didn't I say that, Tom?'

'Yes,' Hayes said, tapping another yawn.

'Do hotels for him, Tom. Maybe that'll give him the idea.'

'Hotels,' Hayes read. 'Sot, lost, hose, stole, shoe. Hotel so hot she shot host . . . I'm tired.' He sagged in his chair.

'A lost mood, see?' Jordan tried to express it with a gesture of his hands. 'You got to feel it like a child. Do you feel it?'

'I certainly do,' I said.

'What are you tired for, Tom?' Jordan gave his friend a worried glance.

'I don't know,' Hayes said. 'It just seems a little thin, somehow.'

'What does?'

'Mice in chimes. It seems a little thin.'

'What's he talking about?' Jordan asked me.

'I mean when you get to thinking of the hare twisting in the frozen grass and the mastiff bitch in the moonshine cold,' Hayes said.

'What the *hell's* he talking about?' Jordan almost wailed.

'What's-his-name and Keats,' I said.

Jordan made a small, despairing gesture. 'Do phrase,' he pleaded.

'Oh, for God sake!' Hayes got up and went to the radio.

'Don't wake Alice,' I said.

'Do phrase and then we'll get the hell out,' Jordan said.

'Do phrase,' I insisted quickly.

'Explain about it first in its own words,' Jordan said. 'You know.'

'O.K., O.K.' Hayes sighed and sat down. 'You don't have to

dwell on the parse phase, the sharp rasp, the rape shape,' he droned.

'Now show him where Tenniel and What's-his-name, the *douanier*, come in,' Jordan said eagerly.

'In the apes and the asp and the hares,' Hayes went on. 'In the peas and the pears and the tea, in the seraph and the harp.'

Jordan's eyes glowed, like a cat's in a barn. 'Tenniel and What's-his-name, the *douanier*,' he said in a throaty voice.

'Come on, let's go, I got to go,' Hayes said, getting up.

'You didn't have a hat,' I told him.

'Take the oranges and gibbons of What's-his-name,' Jordan went on, in a rapt croak.

'Rousseau, for God sake,' Hayes said. 'Come on.'

Jordan got to his feet. His eyes moved slowly around the room.

'You didn't have a hat,' Hayes said. 'Come on.'

He got Jordan just outside the living-room door. Four more steps would have taken them through the hall to the front door.

'Where do you get the tea in phrase?' I asked suddenly. 'There isn't any "t" in phrase.'

Jordan turned and loped back to his chair and sat down hard, like a tired setter. 'A posset for the highway!' he bawled.

'You asked for this,' Hayes told me wearily.

'Mix him a short one,' I said.

Hayes went slowly back into the living room and I closed the door behind him. I knew Alice was standing at the head of the stairs in the dark. 'What *is* it?' she whispered.

'A posset for the highway,' I told her.

'Jink Jordan? Oh, no!' She went back to her room.

I lingered in the hall, hoping they would come out, but Jordan's voice was loud and argumentative. 'Will you stop saying it's thin, for God sake?' he shouted.

'All right, all right, it's exiguous, then,' Hayes said.

'It's exiguous because it's undeveloped, that's why,' Jordan replied. 'You can't develop a thing like this in one night.'

I went back into the room and shut the door behind me. Jordan was sitting in the chair I had been in, pulling some papers out of his inside coat pocket.

'Put that stuff away,' Hayes commanded him sharply.

'Just a second,' Jordan said. 'I knew we'd left something out. How in the hell could you let me leave Blake out?' He began to pore over a pencilled scrawl on the back of a typewritten page.

'We proved Blake had it,' he said loudly. 'We proved Blake knew all about it, and here it is!'

Hayes grabbed the sheet of paper away from him. 'If I read it, will you get up and go home?' he asked. 'And don't drink that so fast.'

'Read it,' Jordan said, waving his glass. 'Wait a minute!' He pointed a finger at me. 'How many tigers are there in—what's the line, Tom?'

' "Tiger! Tiger! burning bright in the forests of the night",' Tom recited.

'One tiger,' I said. 'How many Toms are there in "Tom, Tom, the piper's son"?'

Jordan set his drink down and waved his arms despairingly. 'Journalist!' he said bleakly.

'This is kind of interesting,' Hayes said hurriedly. 'There are actually five tigers in the first two lines of the poem – that is, the necessary letters are repeated often enough to spell the word five times, three times in addition to "tiger, tiger", with a couple of "t"s and an "i" left over.'

Jordan finished his drink in a gulp. 'Nursery rhymes!' he said bitterly.

'In those two lines,' Hayes cut in, 'Blake used only twelve letters of the alphabet, so Jink thinks he was on to the new dimension.'

'Thinks!' Jordan cried.

'Wordsworth, who was not on to it,' Hayes continued, 'used nineteen letters in "She dwelt among the untrodden ways, beside the springs of Dove".'

Jordan shook his head at me slowly. 'It'll take me ten years to work this thing out,' he snarled, 'and you giggle at it like a girl. Tell him about Planters Peanuts, Tom.'

Hayes handed the sheet of paper back to Jordan and ran his hand over his forehead. 'There are nine letters in Planters Peanuts, or only three fewer than Blake used in those two lines. Come on, let's go.'

'One more, maybe?' Jordan said, holding out his glass.

'I'm going,' Hayes snapped. 'I'll wait just two minutes for you in the car.' He walked over and opened the door, closed it behind him, went out the front door, got in the car, and slammed the car door shut.

'There goes one of the sweetest characters in the whole world,' Jordan said.

I started turning out the table lamps, and Jordan got to his feet.

'So long, Jink,' I said. He walked slowly to the door, opened it, and said over his shoulder, 'Not in a million years.' The only light left on now was the one in the hall. Jordan closed the front door after him with great care. After a moment, the engine started and the car drove off.

Half an hour later, in bed, I had almost dropped off when, in the narrow strip of lucidity between the bright compound of consciousness and the dark jungle of sleep, I remembered, with a start like a gunshot, the tiger in the three six-letter words. I tried all the permutations I could think of, using one consonant after another, from 'b' to 'z.' I couldn't fit the tiger into any six-letter word except tigers, and that obviously didn't count. I began all over again: tibger, bitger, grebit, trebig, briget, ticger, grecit, gercit, tidger, gertid, dregit.

The dawn was fluttering at the window when I finally found the three words, one after another, with tiger in them.

Alice woke up. 'Haven't you been to sleep yet?' she asked.

'Gaiter, goiter, aigret,' I said. 'Avoid the consonants. It's as simple as that.'

'Go to sleep,' she said.

I managed it finally. It wasn't easy.

AUTHOR'S NOTE: Shortly after the foregoing story appeared in *The New Yorker* the editors received and passed on to me a letter written by Mr George Rose Smith, an eminent tiger hunter of Little Rock, Arkansas. Mr Smith's letter went in part as follows: 'In James Thurber's recent story, Here Come the Tigers, his friends assured him that there are three six-letter words containing the letters t-i-g-e-r. Thurber spent a sleepless night in tracking down the tigers in gaiter, goiter and aigret, and apparently concluded that he had exhausted the possibilities . . . Disturbed by the thought that the tiger is as near to extinction as Thurber intimates, I sent two native beaters through the Websterian veldts and quickly bagged the limit of ten.

'The girt group of words is infested with the beasts, both girted and begirt being perfectly good usage. For some reason engirt is branded as obsolete, though it happens that we in the South have occasion to use it almost daily. The prefix re- conceals two fine tigers, in regilt and regift. In the latter the prefix is used in the sense of 'back to an original or former position,' so that regift is closely allied to the familiar concept of an Indian giver . . .

The suffix -er is also good for two tigers. Tigger is an attractive word, which the lexicographer (probably late for a date) hurriedly defined as "one who tigs". Tig itself means to run about, as cattle pestered by flies. Pestered by tigers is doubtless historically correct, but such tigging doesn't become habitual. Our lexicographer spent more time on tinger, defining it as "one who or that which tinges". We do not seem to have any word for one who, or even that which, tings. Perhaps the best choice would be ting-er, the hyphen giving a subtle indication of the tiger's stripes. The definition of gitter, a foreign word for a kind of grating, already carries this connotation of straight lines.

'A rare tiger is preserved in the Scotch word erting, which means urging on – a derivation from a root meaning to tease or provoke. This ancient custom of teasing or provoking tigers, while not mentioned in modern histories of Scotland, was probably a tribal method of demonstrating bravery.

'Thurber and his companions were interested in finding animals in odd places, as the mice in chimes and the cats in crystal, but they completely overlooked the tiger in a six-letter animal, the common or garden variety of grivet. As every schoolboy knows, the grivet is an intelligent and docile monkey, having a dull olive-green back . . .'

The Figgerin' of Aunt Wilma

When I was a boy, John Hance's grocery stood on the south side of Town Street, just east of Fourth, in the Central Market region of Columbus, Ohio. It was an old store even then, forty-five years ago, and its wide oak floor boards had been worn pleasantly smooth by the shoe soles of three generations of customers. The place smelt of coffee, peppermint, vinegar, and spices. Just inside the door on the left, a counter with a rounded glass front held all the old-fashioned penny candies – gumdrops, liquorice whips, horehound, and the rest – some of them a little pale with age. On the rear wall, between a barrel of dill pickles and a keg of salt mackerel in brine, there was an iron coffee grinder, whose handle I was sometimes allowed to turn.

Once, Mr Hance gave me a stick of Yucatan gum, an astonishing act of generosity, since he had a sharp sense of the value of a penny. Thrift was John Hance's religion. His store was run on a strictly cash basis. He shared the cost of his telephone with the Hays Carriage Shop, next door. The instrument was set in a movable wooden cubicle that could be whirled through an opening in the west wall of the store. When I was ten, I used to hang around the grocery on Saturday afternoons, waiting for the telephone to disappear into the wall. Then I would wait for it to swing back again. It was a kind of magic, and I was disappointed to learn of its mundane purpose – the saving of a few dollars a month.

Mr Hance was nearly seventy, a short man with white hair and a white moustache and the most alert eyes that I can remember, except perhaps Aunt Wilma Hudson's. Aunt Wilma lived on South Sixth Street and always shopped at Mr Hance's store. Mr Hance's eyes were blue and capable of a keen concentration that could make you squirm. Aunt Wilma had black agate eyes that moved restlessly and scrutinised everybody with bright suspicion. In church, her glance would dart around the congregation seeking out irreverent men and women whose expressions showed that they were occupied with worldly concerns, or even carnal thoughts, in the holy place. If she lighted on a culprit, her heavy, dark brows would lower, and her mouth would tighten in righteous disapproval. Aunt Wilma was as honest as the day is long and

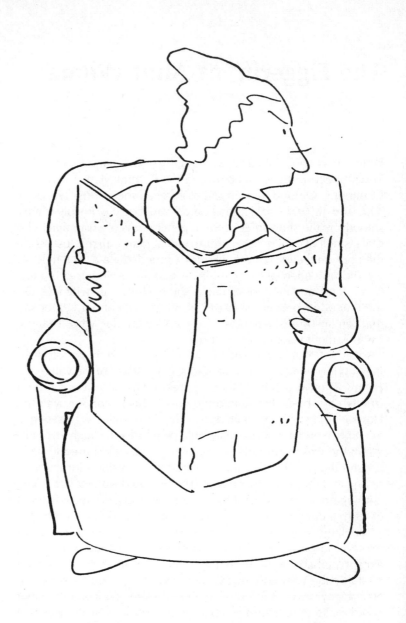

as easily confused, when it came to what she called figgerin', as the night is dark. Her clashes with Mr Hance had become a family legend. He was a swift and competent calculator, and nearly fifty years of constant practice had enabled him to add up a column of figures almost at a glance. He set down his columns swiftly on an empty paper sack with a stubby black pencil. Aunt Wilma, on the other hand, was slow and painstaking when it came to figgerin'. She would go over and over a column of numbers, her glasses far down on her nose, her lips moving soundlessly. To her, rapid calculation, like all the other reckless and impulsive habits of men, was tainted with a kind of godlessness. Mr Hance always sighed when he looked up and saw her coming into his store. He knew that she could lift a simple dollar transaction into a dim and mystic realm of confusion all her own.

I was fortunate enough to be present one day in 1905 when Mr Hance's calculating and Aunt Wilma's figgerin' came together in memorable single combat. She had wheedled me into carrying her market basket, on the ground that it was going to be too heavy for her to manage. Her two grandsons, boys around my own age, had skipped out when I came to call at their house, and Aunt Wilma promptly seized on me. A young'un, as she called everybody under seventeen, was not worth his salt if he couldn't help a body about the house. I had shopped with her before, under duress, and I knew her accustomed and invariable route on Saturday mornings, when Fourth Street, from Main to State, was lined with the stands of truck gardeners. Prices were incredibly low in those days, but Aunt Wilma questioned the cost, the quality, and the measure of everything. By the time she had finished her long and tedious purchases of fresh produce from the country, and we had turned east into Town Street and headed for Mr Hance's store, the weight of the market basket was beginning to pain my arm. 'Come along, child, come along,' Aunt Wilma snapped, her eyes shining with the look of the Middle Western housewife engaged in hard but virtuous battle with the wicked forces of the merchandising world.

I saw Mr Hance make a small involuntary gesture with his right hand as he spied Aunt Wilma coming through the door. He had just finished with a customer, and since his assistant was busy, he knew he was in for it. It took a good half-hour for Aunt Wilma to complete her shopping for groceries, but at length everything she wanted was stacked on the counter in sacks and cans and boxes. Mr Hance set deftly to work with his paper sack and pencil, jotting down the price of each article as he fitted it into the basket. Aunt Wilma watched his expert movements closely, like a hostile baseball fan waiting for an error in the infield. She regarded adroitness in a man as 'slick' rather than skilful.

Aunt Wilma's purchases amounted to ninety-eight cents. After writing down this sum, Mr Hance, knowing my aunt, whisked the paper bag around on the counter so that she could examine his addition. It took her some time, bending over and peering through her glasses, to arrive at a faintly reluctant corroboration of his figgerin'. Even when she was satisfied that all was in order, she had another go at the column of numbers, her lips moving silently as she added them up for the third time. Mr Hance waited patiently, the flat of his hands on the counter. He seemed to be fascinated by the movement of her lips. 'Well, I guess it's all right,' said Aunt Wilma, at last, 'but everything *is* so dear.' What she had bought for less than a dollar made the market basket bulge. Aunt Wilma took her purse out of her bag and drew out a dollar bill slowly and handed it over, as if it were a hundred dollars she would never see again.

Mr Hance deftly pushed the proper keys of the cash register, and the red hand on the idicator pointed to $·98. He studied the cash drawer, which had shot out at him. 'Well, well,' he said, and then, 'Hmm. Looks like I haven't got any pennies.' He turned back to Aunt Wilma. 'Have you got three cents, Mrs Hudson?' he asked.

That started it.

Aunt Wilma gave him a quick look of distrust. Her Sunday suspicion gleamed in her eyes. '*You* owe *me two cents,*' she said sharply.

'I know that, Mrs Hudson,' he sighed, 'but I'm out of pennies. Now, if you'll give me three cents, I'll give you a nickel.'

Aunt Wilma stared at him cautiously.

'It's all right if you give him three cents and he gives you a nickel,' I said.

'Hush up,' said Aunt Wilma. 'I'm figgerin'.' She figgered for several moments, her mouth working again.

Mr Hance slipped a nickel out of the drawer and placed it on the counter. 'There is your nickel,' he said firmly. 'Now you just have to give me three cents.'

Aunt Wilma pecked about in her purse and located three pennies, which she brought out carefully, one at a time. She laid them on the counter beside the nickel, and Mr Hance reached for them. Aunt Wilma was too quick for him. She covered the eight cents with a lean hand. 'Wait, now!' she said, and she took her hand away slowly. She frowned over the four coins as if they were a difficult hand in bridge whist. She ran her lower lip against her upper teeth. 'Maybe if I give you a dime,' she said, 'and take the eight cents . . . It is *two* cents you're short, ain't it?'

Mr Hance began to show signs of agitation. One or two amused customers were now taking in the scene out of the corners of their eyes. 'No, no,' said Mr Hance. 'That way, you would be making me a present of seven cents!' This was too much for Aunt Wilma. She couldn't understand the new and preposterous sum of seven cents that had suddenly leaped at her from nowhere. The notion that she was about to do herself out of some money staggered her, and her eyes glazed for a moment like a groggy prizefighter's. Neither Mr Hance nor I said anything out of fear of deepening the tangle. She made an uncertain move of her right hand and I had the wild thought that she was going to give Mr Hance one of the pennies and scoop up the seven cents, but she didn't. She fell into a silent clinch with the situation and then her eyes cleared. 'Why, of *course*!' she cried brightly. 'I don't know what got into me! You take the eight cents and give me a dime. Then I'll have the two cents that's coming to me.' One of the customers laughed, and Aunt Wilma cut him down with a swift glare. The diversion gave me time to figure out that whereas Mr Hance had been about to gain seven cents, he was now going to lose a nickel. 'That way, I would be making *you* a present of *five* cents, Mrs Hudson,' he said stiffly. They stood motionless for several seconds, each trying to stare the other down.

'Now, here,' said Mr Hance, turning and taking her dollar out of the still open cash drawer. He laid it beside the nickel and the pennies. 'Now, here,' he said again. 'You gave me a dollar three, but you don't owe me a dollar three – you owe me five cents less than that. Here is the five cents.' He snatched it up and handed it to her. She held the nickel between thumb and forefinger, and her eyes gleamed briefly, as if she at last comprehended the peculiar deal, but the gleam faded. Suddenly she handed him his nickel and picked up her dollar and her three cents. She put the pennies back in her purse. 'I've rung up the ninety-eight cents, Mrs Hud- son,' said Mr Hance quickly. 'I must put the dollar back in the till.' He turned and pointed at the $·98 on the indicator. 'I tell you what. If you'll give me the dollar, I'll give you the nickel and we'll call it square.' She obviously didn't want to take the nickel or give up the dollar, but she did, finally. I was astounded at first, for here was the penny-careful Mr Hance knocking three cents off a bill, but then I realised he was afraid of losing the dollar and was willing to settle for the lesser of two evils.

'Well,' said Aunt Wilma irritably, 'I'm sure I don't know what you're trying to do.'

I was a timid boy, but I had to plunge into the snarl, if only on behalf of the family honour. 'Gee, Aunt Wilma,' I told her, 'if you keep the nickel, he's giving you everything for ninety-five cents.'

Mr Hance scowled hard at me. He was afraid I was going to get him in deeper than he already was. 'It's all right, son,' he said. 'It's all right.' He put the dollar in the till and shoved the drawer shut with a decisive bang, but I wasn't going to give up.

'Gee whiz, Aunt Wilma,' I complained, 'you still owe him three cents. Don't you see that?'

She gave me the pitying glance of a superior and tired intelligence. 'I never owed him three cents in my life,' she said tartly. 'He owes me two cents. You stay out of things you don't understand.'

'It's all right,' said Mr Hance again, in a weary voice. He was sure that if she scrabbled in her purse again for the three pennies, she would want her dollar back, and they would be right where they had started. I gave my aunt a look of disenchantment.

'Now, wait!' she cried suddenly. 'Maybe I have the exact change! I don't know what's got into me I didn't think of that! I think I have the right change after all.' She put back on the counter the nickel she had been clutching in her left hand, and then she began to peck at the coins in her purse and, after a good minute, arranged two quarters, four dimes, Mr Hance's nickel, and three pennies on the counter. 'There,' she said, her eyes flashing triumph. 'Now you give me my dollar back.'

Mr Hance sighed deeply, rang out the cash drawer by pushing 'No Sale', and handed her the dollar. Then he hastily scraped up the change, deposited each coin in its proper place in the till, and slammed the drawer shut again. I was only ten, and mathematics was not my best study, but it wasn't hard to figure that Mr Hance, who in the previous arrangement had been out three cents, was now out five cents. 'Good day, Mrs Hudson,' he said grimly. He felt my sympathetic eyes on him, and we exchanged a brief, knowing masculine glance of private understanding.

'Good day, Mr Hance,' said Aunt Wilma, and her tone was as grim as the grocer's.

I took the basket from the counter, and Mr Hance sighed again, this time with relief. 'Good-bye, good-bye,' he said with false heartiness, glad to see us on our way. I felt I should slip him the parsley, or whatever sack in the basket had cost a nickel.

'Come on, child,' said Aunt Wilma. 'It's dreadfully late. I declare it's taken hours to shop today.' She muttered plaintively all the way out of the store.

I noticed as I closed the door behind us that Mr Hance was waiting on a man customer. The man was laughing. Mr Hance frowned and shrugged.

As we walked east on Town Street, Aunt Wilma let herself go. 'I never heard of such a thing in all the born days of my life,' she said. 'I don't know where John Hance got his schooling, if he got any. The very idea – a grown man like that getting so mixed up. Why, I could have spent the whole day in that store and he'd never of figgered it out. Let him keep the two cents, then. It was worth it to get out of that store.'

'*What* two cents, Aunt Wilma?' I almost squealed.

'Why, the two cents he still owes me!' she said. 'I don't know what they teach you young'uns nowadays. Of course he owes me two cents. It come to ninety-eight cents and I give him a dollar. He owed me two cents in the beginning and he still owes me two cents. Your Uncle Herbert will explain it to you. Any man in the world could figger it out except John Hance.'

I walked on beside her in silence, thinking of Uncle Herbert, a balding, choleric man of high impatience and quick temper.

'Now, you let *me* explain it to your Uncle Herbert, child,' she said. 'I declare you were as mixed up as John Hance was. If I'd of listened to you and given him the three cents, like you said, I'd never of got my dollar back. He'd owe me five cents instead of two. Why, it's as plain as day.'

I thought I had the solution for her now, and I leaped at it. 'That's right, Aunt Wilma,' I almost yelled. 'He owed you a nickel and he gave you the nickel.'

Aunt Wilma stabbed me with her indignation. 'I gave *him* the nickel,' she said. 'I put it on the counter right there under your very eyes, and you saw him scoop it up.'

I shifted the market basket to my left arm. 'I know, Aunt Wilma,' I said, 'but it was *his* nickel all the time.'

She snorted. 'Well, he's got his precious nickel, aint he?' she demanded. I shifted the basket again. I thought I detected a faint trace of uneasiness in her tone. She fell silent and quickened her cadence, and it was hard for me to keep up with her. As we turned

south into Sixth Street, I glanced up and saw that she was frowning
and that her lips were moving again. She was rehearsing the story
of the strange transaction for Uncle Herbert. I began to whistle.
'Hush up, child,' she said. 'I'm figgerin'.'

Uncle Herbert was sitting in the living-room, eating an apple. I
could tell from his expression that he was in one of his rare
amiable moods. Aunt Wilma grabbed the basket away from me.
'Now, you let me explain it to your uncle' she said. 'You wait till I
get back.' She sailed out of the room on her way to the kitchen.
A little breathlessly, I told Uncle Herbert the saga of Aunt
Wilma's complicated financial quandary. He was chuckling
when she came back into the room.
Uncle Herbert's amusement nettled her. 'The boy got it wrong,'
she said accusingly. 'He didn't tell it right. He was ever' bit as
mixed up as John Hance.' Uncle Herbert's chuckle increased to
full and open laughter. Aunt Wilma glared at him until he sub-
sided. 'Now, Herbert, you listen to me,' she began, but he cut in
on her.
'If Hance ever gives you that two cents he owes you, Wilma,' he
said, 'I tell you what you have to do to square accounts. Someday
you're going to have to give him a dime for three cents.' He began
to laugh again.
Aunt Wilma Hudson stared at each of us in turn, with a look of
fine, cold scorn, and then she raised both her hands and let them
fall helplessly. 'I declare,' she said, 'I don't know how the world
gets along with the men runnin' it.'

The Lion and the Foxes

The lion had just explained to the cow and goat, and the sheep that the stag they had killed belonged to him, when three little foxes appeared on the scene.

'I will take a third of the stag as a penalty,' said one, 'for you have no hunter's licence.'

'I will take a third of the stag for your widow,' said another, 'for that is the law.'

'I have no widow,' said the lion.

'Let us not split hairs,' said the third fox, and he took his share of the stag as a withholding tax. 'Against a year of famine,' he explained.

'But I am king of beasts,' roared the lion.

'Ah, then you will not need the antlers, for you have a crown,' said the foxes, and they took the antlers, too.

Moral: It is not as easy to get the lion's share nowadays as it used to be.

The Philosopher and the Oyster

By the sea on a lovely morning strolled a philosopher – one who seeks a magnificent explanation for his insignificance – and there he came upon an oyster lying in its shell upon the sand.

'It has no mind to be burdened by doubt,' mused the philosopher, 'no fingers to work to the bone. It can never say, "My feet are killing me." It hears no evil, sees no television, speaks no folly. It has no buttons to come off, no zipper to get caught, no hair or teeth to fall out.' The philosopher sighed a deep sigh of envy. 'It produces a highly lustrous concretion, of great price or priceless,' he said, 'when a morbid condition obtains in its anatomy, if you could call such an antic, anomalous amorphousness anatomy.' The philosopher sighed again and said, 'Would that I could wake from delirium with a circlet of diamonds upon my fevered brow. Would, moreover, that my house were my sanctuary, as sound and secure as a safe-deposit vault.'

Just then a screaming sea gull swooped out of the sky, picked up the oyster in its claws, carried it high in the air, and let it drop upon a great wet rock, shattering the shell and splattering its occupant. There was no lustrous concretion, of any price whatever, among the debris, for the late oyster had been a very healthy oyster, and, anyway, no oyster ever profited from its pearl.

Morals: Count your own blessings, and let your neighbour count his. Where there is no television, the people also perish.

Midnight at Tim's Place

'Old sundials used to boast, in Latin, and I suppose a few in quiet gardens here and there still do, *"Horas non numero nisi serenas"* – "I count serene hours only".'

'*Et pourquoi pas?*' my wife asked vaguely.

It was our first night home after six months in Europe, and the hour at Tim's was late, and more melancholy than serene. We had just heard of the decline of several friends when the stranger with the empty highball glass and the Latin phrase hopped our table.

'My name is Warren Kirkfield,' he said unconvincingly, holding out a damp right hand.

'I bet his real name is Chase or Psst,' said the pretty young woman on my left. I didn't know who she was, or how she had got there. The newcomer ignored this.

'Sit down,' I said unwarmly. 'Urge up a footstool, loosen your stays, saucer your Scotch.'

'Don't be so cruel,' said my wife, moving over so Kirkfield could sit next to her, across the table from me and the fair unknown. 'Maybe he has a right to be sad – it's a free country. Maybe you can't always be *everything* in it, but you can be that.'

'No politics,' said the young woman, with the faintest of hiccups.

'My name is Keith Maitland,' I lied, 'and this is my wife, the former Geraldine Spinney. The lady on my left is a nameless waif out of the night, a poor windlestraw on the stream of time.'

'Ah thought you-all was Bing Crosby,' said the windlestraw, in a fake Dixie that was not too bad for one in her cups. Fake Dixie always enchants me after midnight. I prayed God to keep my hand off her knee.

'Everybody is in the groove tonight,' my wife explained. 'Everybody is just another Gabriel Heatter.'

Suddenly we all had a fresh drink. 'How are you, Bing?' asked Kirkfield, clinking his glass against mine.

'*Non sum qualis eram sub regno bony Sinatra,*' I said quickly, having waited for years to wedge that line in somewhere.

'You finally made it,' my wife said, for she knows all my lines, wedged and unwedged.

'You're just a goddam kissing bug,' the windlestraw told Kirkfield. 'I saw you.' She turned to me. 'I can't leave him alone a minute but what he's bending some girl over backward. This one had glasses and too much teeth.'

'I was being a gentleman,' protested Kirkfield. 'The lady had something in her eye.'

'What was it?' asked Mrs Kirkfield, for it was unquestionably she. 'A roguish twinkle?'

'I came here to tell these charming people a sad story, not to refight the war between the sexes,' Kirkfield said.

'Oh, my God! Not that story again,' said his wife.

I had lost interest in her knee. 'Go ahead, Maitland,' I said.

'Just call me plain Keith,' he murmured.

'The people at the next table must think they are losing their minds,' my wife put in.

'Or ours,' Mrs Kirkfield amended.

'Well, then,' Kirkfield began, 'I was on the edge of a nervous crackup last summer, for the usual variety of reasons – fear of death, fear of life, fear of the inhuman being. Also, I had just become forty-one, and realized that I only had nineteen years to live before I would begin to cackle.'

'I won't be there,' said his wife's voice, from inside her highball glass. 'He'll be bald as a beagle and his back will hurt and he'll babble about his conquex.'

'Quests,' my wife corrected her.

'You can say that again,' said Mrs Kirkfield.

'There was only one person I wanted to see, wanted to talk to,' Kirkfield went on. 'The greatest symbol of security in my life, the

man who could pull me back from the doors of Hell, my old philosophy professor, Dr Pensinger. I had not seen him for five years, but for nearly twenty we had exchanged postcards at Christmas and, because it amused him – you know how professors are – on Nietzsche's birthday.'

'I got to have more whisky to get through this again,' said his wife, and we got more whisky.

'Everybody, in college and afterwards, turned to Dr Pensinger for inspiration and consolation,' her husband went on. 'He had, and still has, some piece of unique philosophy for each special case. "You can keep a stiff upper lip, and smile, too", and "Don't let that chip on your shoulder be your only reason for walking erect". We always left Dr Pensinger's study with a high heart and renewed hope.'

'I just won't be there, that's all,' his wife cut in. 'Let him stomp his cane and yell his head off, for all I care. Give me a man like Gary Cooper or Harpo Marx, who doesn't talk for God's sake all the time.'

I touched her glass with mine, and said, 'Here's something in your eye, I hope.'

'Much he'd care if you did,' she said.

'Well, last summer, when I got the galloping jumps, I decided to call on Dr Pensinger and see if he could pull me out of it,' Kirkfield said. 'He lives in a charming house in Riverdale, and I drove up there one Sunday afternoon. His wife opened the door, and said,

"We don't need anything today." Before she could shut the door, I told her who I was and why I was there, and she said Dr Pensinger was in his study and I could just go on in, and so I did. It was a terrifying visit. He had not changed a bit. He did not even seem a day older than the last time I had met him and listened to his cheering words. The same thoughful blue eyes, the same reassuring smile, the same gentle voice.' Kirkfield took a great gulp of his highball.

'Then what was terrifying about the visit?' I asked.

Kirkfield lit a cigarette. 'He was wearing two hats,' he said. There was a long pause.

'In his study?' I asked.

'*Two* hats?' my wife asked, putting her realistic finger on the more incongruous fact.

'Two hats,' Kirkfield repeated. 'They were both grey felt hats, one on top of the other. The terrifying thing was that he didn't say anything about them. He just sat there with two hats on, trying to cheer me up.'

'I always say you can have too much philosophy,' Mrs Kirkfield said. 'It isn't good for you. It's disorganising. Everybody's got to wake up sometime feeling that everything is terrible, because it is.'

'Couldn't you have said, "Pardon me, but you seem to be wearing two hats"?' my wife wanted to know.

'No, I couldn't,' said Kirkfield. 'I don't even remember how I got out of there. I had the chattering jitters. His wife showed me to the door, and said, "Did he buy anything? If he did, I'll simply send it back when it arrives."'

I thought it was time for another drink. We had all finished our last one very quickly.

'We never know what's going to happen to us,' my wife said.

'I don't care if my husband wears *three* hats,' his wife said. 'I won't be there.'

I had a sudden frightening vision of walking about the city in a few years, wearing only one shoe. Even my best friends, I realised, wouldn't mention it. I thought it was time to go home now, and stood up. My wife and I left the Kirkfields sitting there with four drinks, since we had not touched our new ones.

Tim helped me on with my overcoat, and handed me my hat, and we started to the door. One of the waiters came running after me, and handed me a hat. 'You left this the last time you were here,' he said. 'You went away without a hat that night.'

'Don't you dare!' my wife said, but I put the hat he gave me on top of the one I was wearing, and we went out into the street, and I whistled for a taxi. Pretty soon, one drove up and stopped, but when the driver saw that I was wearing two hats, he said, 'Not in this cab, Jack.' He was about to drive off when my wife opened the door and got in. 'I'll see you at the Algonquin,' she said, 'if you get that far.'

I stood there for a long while, and it began to rain. I walked back to the hotel in the rain.

The Other Room

The bar of the Hôtel Continental in Paris is large and comfortable, and never too crowded, especially in October, when the American invaders are beginning to thin out, and it is presided over by an efficient and amiable waiter named Jacques. He had just brought drinks for my wife and me and an English painter we know. You can lean back in the Continental bar, drinking for pleasure, slowly, in the European manner, without the urge to see how soon you can reach the point when you no longer know you're drinking, in the American manner.

An American woman, at a near-by table, was explaining to a friend the reason for her dermatitis, insisting that it had been caused by aluminium pots and pans.

'My allergist says I have an emotional conflict or something,' she said. 'Doctors always say there's something the matter with you, but it's almost always something you use around the house, or wear, or eat. Of course, I'm terribly high-strung, I know that,' she said, 'but it isn't that. If it was I'd know it.'

The Continental bar, like any other place where Americans gather, is used largely for the exchange of symptoms, complaints about French coffee, and the enumeration of hotels and restaurants on the Continent and in England which one should, at all costs, avoid.

We were waiting for three persons to join us, all of them compatriots of ours – one a twenty-two-year-old American girl, the daughter of friends of ours back home, and the other two a man and his wife, friends of friends of ours, neither of whom we had ever met. We had got, a few days before, the usual note from somebody in New York, saying that she had instructed the Barretts to look us up at the hotel, and, in the unfailing routine of such matters, they had telephoned and we had made a date for drinks, hoping they would not recite too many symptoms or complaints before we could get rid of them.

The painter was telling us about his own favourite hotel, a mythical composite one, invented in the imagination of a friend of his, and called the Hôtel Pas-de-Calais-et-Pas-de-Confort, when a nine-year-old girl, unmistakably American, and loose momentarily from her parents, materialised at my elbow. She had dashed into the bar to look at the television set near the door leading into the dining room.

'It's in French,' she said. 'It's in French,' she said. 'It ought to be in English. Why isn't it in English?' I explained to her that it was not in English in the same way that television in America was not in French, but she was unconvinced and clearly unimpressed by my knowledge of such things. The small interruption annoyed me, because I had been on the point of describing my own favourite French hostelry, the Hôtel-de-l'Univers-et-de-Massachusetts.

'Tell me a story,' commanded the little girl. 'My name is Eunice.' She squirmed into a chair and stared at me.

'Well, did you ever hear of the Teapot Dome scandal?' I asked.

'I don't think I like it,' she said. 'What is it?'

'You surely know what a teapot dome is,' I said. She got up, frowning, stood on her toes a moment, and sat down again. 'Yes,' she said.

I began to drink faster, in the American manner, and said, 'A scandal is when a teapot dome doesn't obey its parents, but runs in and out of bars, and won't eat anything for bekkus except lint and buttons. Well, this particular teapot dome was—'

A large woman, obviously the child's mother, loomed suddenly out of nowhere, like a pirate ship. 'We never say bekkus to Eunice,' she said. 'She loathes it.'

'I loathe it,' said Eunice.

'Sorry,' I said. 'It has been so long since I was a little girl I have forgotten.'

'Now, now,' said my wife. 'You were going to be nice this evening.'

'For a change,' our painter friend asked, 'or just as a noble experiment?'

'Well!' said the ignored mother, and she dragged the little girl away.

'What happened to the Teapot Dome scandal? You can't just leave it hanging there, you know,' said the painter, but I left it hanging there, for my wife said, 'Here's Linda now.'

Linda Gray, fresh-looking and pretty, with the eyes of an angel, said she was sorry she was late, but I reminded her that American girls were always late, and she was introduced to our English friend.

'Mr Middleton would like to paint you, I am sure,' I said.

'I am a gifted man,' Middleton said, 'but not that gifted. The portrait of this lady would require something more ethereal than paint.'

My wife asked Linda what she would like to drink, and she asked for a Coca-Cola. 'I have had an adventure,' she said. 'Not a very pleasant one.'

'I hope it isn't too racy,' I said. 'My wife has led a cloistered life, and believes that the storks find babies under cabbage leaves.'

'Oh, it wasn't like that,' Linda said, with a slight *frisson*. 'I had just turned away from the window of a shop on the Rue de Rivoli when this American — he must have been about sixty — spoke to me. It's terrible, or sad, or something, but it's usually an American, a middle-aged American, who speaks to us girls on the street, not a Frenchman or any other foreigner.'

'What did he say?' my wife wanted to know. Linda paused a moment. 'He said *"Combien pour toute la nuit?"*' she said.

'He *must* be at least sixty,' I said. 'That goes back to the battle of Paris in the First World War. I know all the verses.'

'You would,' my wife said.

'I used to sing them with the fellows,' I said, 'but I never said them to the girls.'

'I just looked at him,' Linda said, 'and told him, "I am an American girl." I really put my best Sunday virtue into it. Funny, he seemed to look at me and past me too. It was odd, and gave me the shivers a little. Then he said something I didn't understand and walked away.'

'Travel is broadening, but disillusioning,' said Middleton.

'I know the type,' I said, 'for I make a study of morbid things. He probably hadn't made a pass at a woman for twenty years back home. Over here, on summer holiday, they get away from their wives, who are out shopping, and the devil takes hold of them. He was probably just trying to recapture his lost youth. Paris has a strange effect on the middle-aged American male, something like the loss of inhibition that takes place on shipboard. Of course, it happens to the American woman, too, sometimes. I knew a cruise director, once, who told me that he had had affairs with women on ships who wouldn't have spoken to him on land.'

'Human nature, as Montaigne or somebody said years ago, is capable of curious behaviour,' Middleton put in. 'The dark unfathomed caves of notion, to coin a phrase — a rather pretty phrase, if I may say so.'

'My God, there he is now!' said Linda. The man she was looking at had just come into the bar and begun looking around. He was sixty, all right, with a familiar harried look, and the sagging shoulders of a man who has sat for years at a desk.

'I hope it isn't Barrett,' my wife said, but it was Barrett. He headed straight for our table, walking with a slight limp.

'In the midst of life we are in *worse* than death,' Middleton said.

'I'd better go,' Linda said. 'I'd better go.'

'He won't remember you,' I told her. 'Don't recognise him.'

'If he could forget this girl's eyes,' Middleton said, 'he is something less than normal.'

I said, 'Are you Mr Barrett?' before he could say anything, but managed to keep both hands busy, one holding my drink, the other my cigarette. I didn't know what to say, but I had to say something.

'You been behaving yourself, Mr Barrett?' I asked.

'Have to,' he said. 'Got the little woman with me, you know.' We managed the introduction somehow. Barrett recognised Linda, there was no doubt about that. He was for three seconds a statue in bronze, a frightened statue, a little tired, a little older than the man who had walked into the room. My wife did her best to cover it over with roses, asking where Mrs Barrett was, and how she was, and how long they were going to stay, and how our mutual friends in New York were, trying to bring some ease to the bronze figure of a trapped, middle-aged, middle-class American man, whose lack of social resource was as evident as wind on a prairie.

Jacques appeared, and more drinks were ordered, and the ease that Jacques invariably brings to a table of Americans helped a little to break the tableau and the spell.

'I'll have a Scotch and soda, this time,' Linda said.

'Do that twice,' Barrett said, and it seemed to me I had known he was going to say just that. Middleton sat studying us all as if he were about to sketch in a composition, a conversation piece.

Barrett sat down stiffly and uneasily on the edge of a chair, the unhappiest man I had seen that summer – or any other summer, for that matter. I felt enormously sorry for him.

'Were you in the First World War, the war the French still call "*La Grande Guerre*"?' I asked, and he sat back a little and came as close as he could to relaxing.

'I was there, Charley,' he said, almost as if to himself. 'This is the first time I have seen Paris since those days. I was at Fère-en-Tardenois, and I got shoved around up there. It was pretty rough going.'

'Never rougher anywhere,' I agreed. 'I knew two guys who were there,' and I told him their names, but I don't think he was listening. 'Yeah, sure, yeah, sure,' he said. 'The Heinies knocked off a lot of us. It was like fighting in a room. They were on all sides of you. I drove out there the other day, hired a car and drove out there. As I got closer to the battlefield, I got scared, I don't mind saying. I wanted to tell the guy to turn around and drive back to Paris, but I didn't. We came to this sign that says "Fère-en-Tardenois—14 km."; and it seemed like two hours from there. There's a big American cemetery there now.' He was glad to get the Scotch he had ordered, but his hand shook when he picked it up.

'One of the men I knew was made a sergeant on the field,' I said. 'All the sergeants of his company had been killed. He got out of it alive, but he carried shrapnel with him all his life, and was in and out of hospitals.'

'Yeah, sure,' said Barrett. 'I got some stuff in me, too. I got a silver plate, I got two silver plates.' He touched his right leg and then the left side of his head. 'It seems to me I was always in hospitals, army hospitals, in my twenties.' He gave me a troubled sigh. 'What I seem to remember most is hospitals. When I get nightmares, even my office turns into a hospital, even now.'

There was a softening of the tension in the air, a little, I thought, like candlelight replacing the glare of torches. Nobody said anything for a moment except Linda. 'I'm sorry,' Linda said.

'Where is Mrs Barrett?' my wife asked, tactfully shifting gears.

'I don't know,' Barrett said. 'I was to meet her here. She's always on time, she's always ahead of me.'

'Perhaps she left a message for you at the desk,' my wife said. 'Shall I find out?'

Barrett stood up, saying, 'No, no, I'll go out and ask,' and he went out of the bar.

'He's kind of nice,' said Linda, after a long moment. 'He has a nice smile. I wish he had smiled when he spoke to me on the street, but he didn't.'

'I think he needs another drink,' I said. Barrett had finished his drink fast, as nervous men do, and so I signalled Jacques. 'The same again, all around,' I told him.

'I don't know anything about him or his wife,' my wife put in. 'All that Ella said in her note was something about "Please be nice to the Barretts. They have both been through a lot. I'll tell you about it later." Ella signed the letter "Hastily". Everybody is always in such a rush.'

'You never know what the boys who survived Fère-en-Tardenois are going to say or do,' I said, 'or how much they are going to drink. You've either been through a battle like that, or you haven't.'

'I don't think he should have driven up there,' Linda said. 'I don't think it was good for him.'

'I do,' Middleton said. 'Maybe he'll get it out of his nightmares, now. Maybe his office will turn into an office again in his dreams.'

Barrett came back to the table, looking even more tired, and somehow greyer. 'Martha is lying down,' he told us. 'This trip has pretty well tuckered her out. We shouldn't have done that châteaux tour, I guess. It took a lot out of her.' He didn't sit down. 'Well, thank you for the drink,' he said. 'It was nice of you to ask us.'

'You're not going yet,' I told him. 'We've ordered you another drink.' His face brightened a little and, after a slight pause, he sat down again, this time farther back in his chair.

'Tell us some more about the war,' I said. 'Maybe it will get those hospitals out of your nightmares.' He gave us his slow, gentle smile. 'It wasn't so much the battle, or even hospitals,' he began, finally. 'At least, that's what one of the docs in the States told me back in the twenties. It was something that happened in the battle of Paris, I guess. Anyway, this doc said so.' The new drinks arrived, and he picked his up eagerly.

'What was it?' Linda asked.

'Kind of a silly thing, it was,' he said. 'We come from Iowa, you know, Cedar Rapids. I was only twenty-one when I got to France, and I thought it was a million miles from anywhere. You get homesick when you're that young, and are that far away from home. It's worse than the battle. You get through the battle somehow, and you don't think much about it till later in the hospital, or when you fall asleep. They had given me a lot of stuff to make me sleep, and I'd never taken dope before.' He drank some more of his whisky and soda. 'I remember Paris clearer than anything,' he said, 'but I can't remember how I got here, or just when it was. I got out of the base hospital, because I couldn't take it any longer, and I got to Paris. I was AWOL. It's all pretty hazy.'

After this confession, he sat for a long time without saying anything, and we waited.

'I remember walking along the Champs-Elysées,' he began

finally. 'I never could pronounce it right.' He was correct about
that, but none of us pronounced the words for him. 'Then, there
was this girl, this French girl. She wasn't any older than I was. She
spoke English, though, and was I glad for that! Well, we sat out in
front of the Café de la Paix. We drove there in a taxi. She said she
thought I didn't look very well, and she said she thought I should
have something to drink. And so we had a couple of drinks. Then
she told me about herself. She came from some place in Southern
France, and her father was a drunkard, and used to beat up the
family on Saturday nights, so she ran away to Paris, and got some
work in a garment factory, but all they gave her was a few francs a
week, and she saw all these other girls in fur coats and things, and
so she took to—well, making the boys feel better, she called it.'
This time, there was an even longer silence, but we all waited
politely and attentively.

'I never told Martha about all this,' he took up again. 'But the
other day I took a taxi up to the street where this French girl used to
have an apartment. I remembered the street, and even the
number, I remembered the number, too. They call it Rue Mar-
cadet, and it's up there in Montmartre. I didn't get out of the cab.
Maybe I should have, but I didn't get out. I just looked at the
building, the windows on the second floor. Nobody there would
know about her now. Her name was Françoise, but she told me to
call her Frances, and so I called her Frances. She would be sixty
now. Doesn't seem possible, but she would be sixty now. Well,
like I said, she was only twenty herself then, but there were
pictures of guys all over her living room, guys in uniform, guys of
all the allied countries. The picture I can't forget was a picture of a
young Canadian soldier. She had it framed, and it was sitting on
her piano. He was a handsome fella, and he couldn't have been
more than twenty himself.' He looked at Linda, as if she were too
young hear the rest of the story, but she said, 'I'm much older than
any of you were. I'm twenty-two.'

'Well, of course, I never saw the Canadian boy, but he gets into
my dreams, too, kinda banged up, with his uniform all bloody.
You see, she found out from a buddy of his later that he had been
killed in action. This friend of his brought her this note he had
written her, the last note he had ever written, I guess. She showed
it to me one day in her apartment – the first and only time I ever
went there,' he added hastily. 'I remember what it said, all right,
every word of it, though I don't remember things as well as I used
to.' He took some more of his drink and set the glass on the table.

'Finish that,' I told him, 'and we'll get another one.'

'No, no,' he said, with his little smile, 'I never have more than two. Well, she had a bottle of port wine at her place, and we sat there drinking this port wine, too much of it, I guess. After a while, she went out of the room into – the other room, and left me sitting there with the whole damn war all around me, it seemed like. This good-looking boy on the piano kept staring at me, and looking sad, and awful young – like that part from St James Infirmary''.'

' "So young, so cold, so fair,'' ' Linda murmured.

'Yeah, that's it,' Barrett said. He picked up his glass again, and leaned back in his chair, and sighed deeply. 'Well, I sat there, thinking of too many things, thinking of everything, the way it all floods back on you, you know.' We all nodded together. 'I thought of a girl back home in Iowa, who was only seventeen then, I thought of Martha. Then I heard this French girl calling to me from – the other room.' He sat forward again, and seemed to stiffen, and his voice, when he spoke again, seemed very far away. 'Well, I got up and left the place. I guess I kinda ran out on her. It wasn't until I got into the street that I realised I was carrying my glass, and it still had some port wine in it. I put it down somewhere, and went on walking. I must've walked for miles. The next thing I really remember I was back at the hospital. I guess the MP's got me.'

He broke off his recital to finish his drink, and then he stood up. 'After that, for a while, I went into a nose dive, kinda what the docs call nervous prostitution,' he (and Sigmund Freud) said. None of us laughed, or even smiled. 'There were a lot of songs we all sang in those days,' he said, 'some of them, well, kinda naughty, as the ladies say. I was thinking of them today, walking around Paris, I was thinking about a lot of things. Seemed like it was 1918 again, and I was young and back in Paris.' He picked up his glass from the table and drained the last drop, and set it down again. 'This girl, this Frances, gets in my dreams sometimes too. But the door is always locked, or something, or the floor to the other room is gone, like it was blown away.'

'All doors open sooner or later. Maybe this one will now,' I said, trying to be cheerful.

'Well,' Barrett said, 'you've all been very nice to me today, and I appreciate it, and I know Martha will, too. I wish you could meet Martha. She's very sweet. I don't know what I would have done without Martha. She's got me through a lot of things.'

'Oh, we'll see you again,' my wife said, 'and Martha, too. Tell her I'll send her some flowers. How long are you going to be here?'

'Three days,' Barrett said, 'three days, and then we're sailing back on the *Liberté*. I like the French ships, I like France.'

Linda suddenly stood up, and ran, rather than walked, around the table. She was tall, in the manner of American girls of today, almost as tall as Barrett, so she did not have to stand on tiptoe when she kissed him on the forehead. 'I like you, too,' she said, warmly. 'I think you're lovely.' He patted her hand twice, and then said something none of us could understand, and hurriedly walked away.

'I'm sixty years old myself,' I said, 'but mighty spry for a man that age, and I'll be even spryer if we have another drink.'

'I should say we all need what you Americans call a flock of drinks,' Middleton said. My wife called Jacques.

Before we left the Continental bar, all of us except Middleton had reached the point where we weren't quite sure we were still drinking. At that point, I have an inveterate tendency to sing, and my wife sensed this moment had come. 'Not here in the bar,' she said. 'You can sing in the cab on the way to the Chope Danton.' in the cab, I said, 'How about "It's a Long Long Way to Tipperary", or "Where a Nightingale Is Swinging and a Pale Moon Beams"?'

'Not that, not one of *them*,' Linda said. 'I want to hear "*Combien pour Toute la Nuit?*"' And so I sang for her, in fair voice, and on key for once in my life, '*Combien pour Toute la Nuit?*'

The Lady from the Land

A recent hostess of mine, who gave an Anglo-American cocktail party for forty persons (at which the customary seventy showed up), had selected for the moist event one of the large rooms on the first floor of a famous London hotel. It was fun, that party, until the woman I shall call the Lady from the Land sat down beside me. Something told me that I was going to be reproved or reproached or upbraided or rebuffed, and something was right. What she had to say, or rather to reiterate, was a complaint about a piece I wrote for *Punch* last year in which I predicted that, if our species didn't look up and behave, the porpoises would come in from the sea and replace us as the chief mammal on earth.

'I don't think God likes you for that,' the lady said. 'She doesn't like people who deride, or degrade, the human species.'

'She?' I asked.

'I've always believed that God is feminine,' she told me. 'As a Woman, She would naturally be interested in Mankind, and would never allow the tortoises to take over, as you call it.'

I choked slightly on the fresh Scotch and soda the waiter had just handed me. 'I did not say tortoises, madam,' I told her. 'I said porpoises.'

She waved this away with an impatient gesture. 'It's the same thing,' she said.

I lit a cigarette and recited 'Listen, my children, and you shall hear of the midnight ride of Paula Revere.'

Our hostess suddenly appeared, carrying a martini, and said to me, in what she intended to be a whisper, 'Don't be profound.' I knew then that the martini was her fourth, and I said to her, 'The girl stood on the burning deck whence all but she had fled.' My hostess fled, but my critic didn't.

'All that you men care about is the sea,' my companion said. 'You hear voices from the sea. I've been doing some research on it, and I know. In *Juno and the Paycock* the Paycock says "The sea is callin' me." Tennyson wrote, "One clear call for me, and may there be no moaning of the bar when I put out to sea."'

'May I—' I began.

'Hear me out,' she said. She took a drink from the waiter's tray and I took two, as she went on talking. 'Robert Adlai Stevenson said—'

'Louis,' I corrected her.

'Don't be rude!' she said. 'I'm no loonier than you are. Stevenson said "Home is the sailor, home from the sea". You men often have to be drafted for war, but you run away to sea. You can hardly wait.'

During her lecture I had kept hearing slight hiccups, and realised that a gentleman guest with several sails in the wind had been listening. 'Let's get it right' he said. 'Stevenson didn't want to be buried at sea. He wrote "Under the wide and starry sky, dig the grave and let me lie. This be the verse you grave for me: here he lies where he longed to be, and he laid him down with a will."'

The intruder began laughing loudly, as he managed to get out of his chair. 'If he laid him down with a will, then he died "intestate",' he chortled, and he went reeling away to tell it to somebody else.

'I hate the word "intestate",' my companion said. 'Why do they have to give old men's diseases such awful names?'

'You are thinking of intestatitis, madam,' I said coldly. 'Intestate means he died without a will.'

'But that man said he died *with* a will,' she said sharply.

I was on the point, I'm afraid, of saying, 'Ah, shut up!' but saved myself just in time, and began on my second drink of the two new ones. She kept right on bickering.

'Your Eugene O'Neill in *Anna Christie* goes on and on about that old devil sea.'

'Davil,' I corrected her, but she said, 'Quibble, quibble.' This time I made her hear *me* out. 'What are you working up to, madam, or away from, may I ask?'

'I'm working up to that silly play by Hendrik Hudson,' she said. 'I mean *The Lady from the Sea*.' I decided to let her make a playwright out of Hendrik Hudson, and just went on drinking. 'Now then, no woman hears the call of the sea. It's just you men. You're all Joseph Conrads and William McFees at heart. I think it's perfectly dreadful that your poet Longfellow, when he wrote about the schooner *Hesperus*, said, "The skipper had brought his little daughter to bear him company." Where was the child's mother all that time?'

'It's an old tradition of the sea that a woman aboard a ship is unlucky,' I told her, 'and it has always turned out that way. You may not know it, but the skipper's wife was aboard the mystery ship, the *Mary Celeste,* which should have been called the *Harry Celeste*, and then nothing would have happened to it.'

'That's right, that's right!' my companion exclaimed. 'Blame everything on us women. You even call your ships "she" so that you can blame it on us when they go down or disappear.'

'If you are writing a monograph about all this,' I said, 'you are wasting you valuable time substituting Scotch for ink.'

I was about to get up and join some people, half of whom were taking Kenneth Tynan apart while the other half kept putting him back together again, when another male guest loomed up in front of me. He held an unlighted cigarette in one hand and a matchbox in the other. 'I've given up smoking,' he said. 'Nobody could make me smoke again, not even my wife when I'm mad at her.' He broke the cigarette in two and tossed it away, and brought out another one, which he put in his mouth. 'You couldn't make me smoke this cigarette, even at gunpoint,' he proclaimed loudly.

I pointed my right index finger at him as if it were a gun barrel and said, 'We'll see about that. Now then, either you smoke that cigarette, sir, or I shall pull the trigger.'

He paused a moment, then lit the cigarette and inhaled deeply. 'You made me smoke,' he snarled. 'Remember that.' And he walked away, inhaling.

This time I took three Scotches from the waiter's tray, put one on the floor near me, and held the other two in my hands. Suddenly another woman was in the chair beside me. She took the highball from my left hand.

'I hear you're crazy about the sea,' she said.

'Crazy is correct,' I told her. 'And it's the only accurate thing I've heard said this evening.'

Her voice became brighter. 'Is it true,' she demanded, 'that if a ship is sinking from too much cargo, they throw the supercargo overboard?'

'That's a lot of jetsam, madam,' I told her. 'They don't have to throw him overboard. He jumps. The sea is calling him.'

At this point my wife appeared, for we had a dinner date. I heard my new companion whisper to her, in a worried tone, 'Your husband thinks that a ship's cargo is human,' And she went away.

'I think we'd better leave now,' my wife said, and I stood up, on a fairly even keel.

'The proper maritime term is shove off,' I told her.

'Why in the world have you been going on about the sea to

everybody?' my wife demanded. 'I hope you'll be all right at dinner,' she added anxiously.

As we started out, the Lady from the Land sailed up to us. I finished the drink I was still carrying, and turned upon her. 'Don't kiss me, Mrs Hardy,' I said brusquely.

My wife took my arm and dragged me away, leaving the Lady standing there speechless for once in her life.

'I simply have to have another drink at the bar,' I told my wife on the way out of the hotel, and we went into the bar. This time I had a straight Scotch, and was beginning to relax when my wife abruptly said, 'I can't understand why they have to keep weighing the anchor on a ship all the time. It's made of iron, and I don't see how its weight could possibly change.' I thought that over for a moment, but didn't say anything, because the bartender was listening intently. After all, I do not want to be committed to a mental institution during this visit of mine to the Port of London.

'Down the hatch!' I said, and we finished our drinks and shoved off.

'That woman you called Mrs Hardy is a brilliant writer,' my wife remarked. 'Didn't you know that?'

'Brilliant, but listing heavily – listing heavily to Scotch,' I said. 'She believes that Ibsen discovered the Hudson River. Nobody gets anything right any more. Mrs Hardy goes around telling everbody that I believe the tortoises are going to take over.'

My wife laughed merrily, and then said, 'To-morrow and to-morrow and to-morrow creeps in this carapace from day to day.'

I knew I couldn't top that, so I went on with her to the dinner party in sulky silence.

Brother Endicott

The man stared at the paper in his typewriter with the bleak look of a rain-soaked spectator at a dull football game, and then ripped it out of the machine. He lit a cigarette, put another sheet of paper in the wringer, and began a letter to his publisher, without salutation: 'Why you imbeciles have to have a manuscript three months ahead of publication is, by god—' And out came that sheet. Somewhere a clock began striking three, but it was drowned out by a sudden upsurge of Paris night noises.

The street noises of Paris, staccato, profundo, momentary and prolonged, go on all through the summer night, as if hostile hosts were fiercely taking, losing, and regaining desperately disputed corners, especially the bloody angle of the Rue de Rivoli and Rue de Castiglione, just beneath the windows of the writer's hotel room. Presently he heard the jubilant coming of the Americans, late but indomitable, sleepless but ever fresh, moving in, like the taxis of the Marne, from the Right Bank and the Left, shouting, laughing, amiably cursing, as they enveloped and captured the lobby of the hotel. They loudly occupied corridors and rooms, leaving the King's English sprawled and bleeding on the barricades of night. A detachment of foot cavalry trooped past the writer's door, one of the men singing 'Louise' in a bad imitation of Chevalier.

American reinforcements kept on arriving at the hotel, and below his window the writer heard a young feminine voice crying, 'For God's sake, Mother, why not? S'only three o'clock!' Her mother's voice cried back at her, 'Your father's dead and so am I—that's why not.' There was no report from the father, and the writer visualised him lying on the sidewalk, his wallet deflated, a spent and valiant victim of the battle of Paris. The writer emptied a clogged ashtray into a metal wastebasket, switched off the lights in the sitting room of his suite and sprawled on one of the twin beds in the other room. 'It may be the Fourth of July to everybody else,' he said aloud, as if talking to someone he didn't like, 'But it's just two weeks past deadline to me.' He turned over the phrase, 'The Fourteenth of Deadline,' decided there was nothing in it, and was about to take off his right shoe when he heard a knock at the door.

He looked at his wristwatch; it was a few minutes past three o'clock.

The late caller was a young woman he had never seen before. She murmured something that sounded like, 'My husband—I thought maybe—' and he stood aside to let her in, apologising for his shirtsleeves. 'I was afraid it was the fellas looking for a tenor,' he said. 'I'm a baritone myself, but out of practice and not in the mood.' He put the lights on again in the sitting room, waved casually at a chair and, just as casually, she sat in it. 'Voici le salon, as they call it,' he said. 'Makes it sound very proper. What can I do for you? My name's Guy Farland.'

'I know,' she said. 'I've heard you typing at night before. I asked at the desk once, and they said you were here. My name is Marie Endicott.'

He reached for his tie and jacket, but she said, with a faint smile, 'Ne vous dérangez pas. It's too warm.'

'Before we get around to your problem,' he said, 'how about a drink?' He moved to a table containing bottles and glasses and an ice bucket. She nodded when he put his hand on the Scotch bottle. 'Not too strong, please,' she said. 'A lot of soda.'

'I mix drinks my own way,' he told her, 'and I'm said to be good at it. Besides, this is my castle.' He took her in as he fixed the highball, figured that she was not more than twenty-three and that she had had quite a few drinks already, rather desperate ones, which she hadn't enjoyed much. He set her drink down on a table beside her chair. 'If I were a younger writer I would say, "She looked like a chic luna moth in her light green evening gown, as she stood there clutching a dainty evening bag." But you weren't clutching it, just holding it,' he said. 'And I'm a middle-aged writer, not a young one.'

She picked up her drink but didn't taste it. 'I've read your Lost Corner four times,' she said. He went back to mix himself a drink, saying, 'It isn't quite that good. I'm trying to finish another book, but you can't think against this goddam racket. I had got used to the Paris taxi horns and their silence makes me edgy. They have cut out the best part of the noise and left in the worst.'

'The goddam motorcycles,' she said tonelessly. He sat down, and they both listened to the tumult outside the window for a moment. 'The noise has loused me up—I choose the precise word for it,' he said. 'It would certainly rain in Verlaine's heart if he could hear it.' She was looking at him as though he were an actor in a spotlight, and he responded with performance. 'I was thinking

how silent Paris must have been the night François Villon vanished into immortality through the snows of yesteryear. If your
husband has vanished, maybe I can help you find him. I'm a
husband myself, and I know where they go. On the Fourth of July,
of course, it's a little harder, especially in a foreign country.' He
had left the door to the suite ajar, and they could hear a male
quartet somewhere down the hall dwelling liquidly on 'The
Sweetheart of Sigma Chi.'

'Edward isn't lost,' she said. 'He's the bass. Edward Francis
Endicott.' She seemed to add a trace of bitters to the name.
'Wisconsin Alpha. They're in Rip Morgan's room, with a couple of
Americans they picked up at this nightclub. Edward and Rip
insisted on singing "On Wisconsin" – I don't know why we
weren't put out – and these strange men knew the words and
joined in, but they are from Illinois, and so then they all sang
"Loyal to You, Illinois." Our honeymoon has been like that ever
since Edward ran into Rip Morgan in Rome.' She gave the word
'honeymoon' a tart inflection. The quartet down the hall now had
'Dear Old Girl' in full swing, and Farland got up and closed the
door. 'They sound a little older than juniors or seniors,' he said,
coming back to his chair. She took a long swallow of her drink and
set the glass down.

'Edward will be forty-six next week,' she said, in the tone of a
patient on a psychiatrist's couch, and Farland leaned back for the
flow he felt was coming. 'He still wears his fraternity pin. He wore
it on his pyjamas on our wedding night. It's the Nelson Merit Pin.
He got in one year for being biggest Boopa Doopa Chi in the
whole damn country. He has a smaller one, too. Fraternity is his
life. Maybe you've heard of Endicott Emblems, Incorporated.
Well, he's the president. They make fraternity pins, and signet
rings, and everything. He goes around all the time, even over here,
with his right hand out like this.' She separated the thumb and little
finger of her right hand from the other fingers. 'He gives everybody
the grip, in the American Express and at the Embassy, and everywhere he sees an American man. I don't know much about
fraternities. I thought it was something men got over, like football
practice. I went to Smith.'

Farland noticed that she kept glancing over her right shoulder at
the door. 'Brother Endicott won't break in on us,' he said reassur-
ingly. 'Quartets never notice that wives are missing. As for my
wife, she's in Italy.'

'I knew she wasn't here,' Marie Endicott said, and Farland

followed her gaze about the room, which must have revealed
instantly to his visitor the lack of a woman's touch. There were
books and papers on the floor, and that unmistakable masculine
rearrangement of chairs and lamps which a man finds comfortable
and a woman intolerable. 'Nancy is going to pick up our daughters in Italy – we have two. They are coming over on one of the
Export ships because they wanted to see Gibraltar. I don't work at
night when Nancy's here. Wives don't think it's healthy.'

'Ellen Morgan went to bed,' said the girl, 'and Edward thinks I'm
in bed, too.' She took several long swallows of her drink this time,
and sat forward in her chair. 'The reason I'm here, the thing is,' she
began, with a flash of firmness, and then leaned back with a
helpless flutter of her left hand. Farland gave her a cigarette and
held a match for her.

'Don't get a blockage,' he said easily. 'I'm the one with the
blockage. I was thinking of throwing the heroine of my novel out
of a window, but you can't do that in novels, only in real life.' The
girl wasn't listening.

'Edward can't stand any foreign country,' she said, 'because it
isn't God's country, and they don't use God's money, and you
can't get God's martinis, or God's anything.' Her eyes drifted
toward an unopened bottle of bourbon on the table. 'Or God's
whisky,' she said. 'Bourbon is God's whisky, you know.'

'He must have trouble getting God's ice, too,' Farland put in,
'especially at this hour.'

'They don't supply soap at most French hotels,' she went on. 'In
the hotel in Le Havre he called downstairs and said, "Some of you
cave dwellers come up here with some soap and make it snappy.
Endicott wants soap." He speaks of himself in the third person a lot
of the time. He doesn't know any French except "combien" and
"trop cher" and "encore la même chose" and 'Où est le cabinet?"
He calls terraces sitdowns, and he's terrible about the new franc.
He says, "Pas si goddam vite" to taxi drivers. He learned what he
calls doughboy French from his brother Harry. Harry is much
older. He was in the First World War. You know doughboy
French? "Restez ici a minute. Je retourner après cet guy partirs."'
She drank some more and went back to brother Harry. 'Harry
thinks he's dying,' she said. 'He thinks he's dying of everything,
but there isn't anything the matter with him. He ought to go to a
psychiatrist, and he actually did once, but the doctor said something like, "If you're not sick, and you think you're sick, you're
sick." And Harry slammed out of his office.'

'Nice slamming,' Farland said. 'I think I would have, too.'

The girl in the green dress took in a long sad breath and exhaled slowly. 'Harry carries a little mirror, like a woman, and keeps looking at his mouth, even in public,' she said. 'He thinks there's something the matter with his uvula.'

'I'm sorry you told me that,' Farland said. 'It is the only part of my body I have never been conscious of. Can you die of uvulitis or something?'

'Harry and his wife were over here,' the girl continued, 'but they flew back last week, thank God. He suddenly got the idea in the middle of the night that his doctor had secretly called Irene and told her he was dying – Harry, I mean. "This is my last vacation," he screamed, waking Irene up. She thought he had lost his mind in his sleep. "I'm not going to die in Naples or any other foreign city!" he yelled. "I'm going to die in Buffalo!" We live in Milwaukee. It isn't far enough from Buffalo.'

'You were just about to tell me why you came here. I don't mean to Europe, I mean to my chambers, tonight—this morning,' Farland said, but she postponed the reason for her call with a wave of her hand. He sat back and let her flow on. 'Edward is a collector,' she said. 'Big heavy things, like goal posts. He's football crazy, too. I though he was really crazy once when we were having a cocktail and he lifted his glass and said, "Here's to Crazy Legs!" That's Roy Hirsch,' she explained. 'One of the Wisconsin gridiron immortals. He also drinks to the Horse. That's Ameche. He's immortal, too.'

'I'm trying to figure out what you saw in Edward Endicott,' Farland said, a flick of impatience in his tone. 'It's supposed to be a human mystery, I know, but there's usually a clue of some kind.'

She gestured with her hand again and frowned. 'He has more drums than anybody else in the world,' she went on. 'He began collecting them when he was a little boy, and now he has African drums and Maori drums and some from the Civil War and one from the Revolution. He even has a drum that was used in the road company of *The Emperor Jones*, and one of the forty or fifty that were used in *Valencia* during a big production number at the Casino de Paris in 1925, I think it was.' She shuddered slightly, as if she heard all the Endicott drums approaching. 'Is collecting goal posts Freudian?' she asked.

Farland decided to think that over while he freshened the drinks. 'I don't think so,' he said. 'Goal posts are trophies, a sign your side won. The Indians had it worked out better, of course.

Scalping the captain of the losing team would be much simpler. Where does he keep the goal posts?'

'In the attic,' she said, 'except for the one in the guest room. It belonged to Southern Cal. or S.M.U., or somebody we didn't expect to beat and did.' She managed a small evil inflection on 'we'.

'All right, let's have it,' Farland said. 'Why did you come here tonight? All this is overture, I can tell that.'

She sat forward suddenly again. 'Tom will be here, I mean right here, in your suite, in a few minutes,' she said, hurriedly. 'He sent me a message by a waiter at the nightclub, while Edward was trying to get the little French orchestra to play "Back in Your Own Back Yard." Tom must have followed me there. I had to think quick, and all I could think of was your room, because you're always up late.'

Farland got up and put on his tie and coat. 'I ought to look more *de rigueur* for Tom,' he said. 'You're not constructing this very well. You don't just hit your readers with a character named Tom. They have a right to know who he is and what he wants.'

'I'm sorry,' she said. 'I mean about asking him to come here. He's awfully difficult, but at least he isn't predictable. He loves to sweep everything off the mantelpiece when he's mad, but he doesn't use a straight razor and strop it all the time, like Edward. Tom and I were engaged for years, but he didn't want to get married until he got through his army service, so we broke up about that. Everybody else got married and went to camp with their husbands. They had four million babies last year, the American girls.'

'American girls often marry someone they can't stand to spite someone they can,' he said. 'That's a pretty rough generalisation, but I haven't got time to polish it up. Is that where Brother Endicott came in?'

'I don't really know what state Tom is in,' she said. 'He just got out of the service, and I was afraid he would follow me here. It's a long story about how I met Edward. I wanted to come back to Paris. You see, I had spent my junior year here, and I loved Paris. Of course, my mother went completely to pieces. I had a job in New York, but every evening when I got home Mother was waiting for me. Sometimes crocked. She always wanted to have a little talk. We had more little talks than all the mothers and daughters in the world. I was going crazy, and then I met Edward. He seemed so strong and silent and—' She groped for a word and came up with 'attentive.' Farland give her another cigarette. 'He wasn't really strong and silent. He was just on the wagon. Tom hadn't written for months, and I thought maybe he had another girl, and Edward promised to bring me to Paris, and so— I don't know.'

'Paris seems to be full of American girls who are hiding out from their mothers,' Farland said. This caused a flash of lightning in her eyes.

'Mother belongs to the damn lost generation,' she said. 'The trouble with the lost generation is it didn't get lost enough. All the damn lost mothers had only one child,' she went on, warming to what was apparently a familiar thesis. 'They all think their daughters are weak enough to do the things they thought they were strong enough to do. So we have to pay for what they did. I'm glad I missed the 1920s. God.'

'They've stopped singing,' Farland said. 'They must be taking a whisky break. How do I fit into this – for Tom, I mean? I don't want to be knocked cold when he gets here. I seem to be in the middle.'

As if it were an entrance cue, there were two sharp raps on the door. Farland hurried out and opened it. A tall young man breezed past him and into the sitting room. 'Are you all right?' he demanded of the girl.

'No,' Farland said. 'Do you want a drink?'

'This is Mr Farland, Mr Gregg,' said Mrs Endicott. Mr Gregg scowled at his host. 'I don't get this,' he said 'What is that baboon doing now? Could I have a straight Scotch?' Farland put some Scotch and ice in a glass and gave it to him.

'They're probably running out of whisky,' the girl said. 'I don't want Edward to find me gone.'

'He might as well get used to it,' said Tom. He began pacing. 'I was hanging around out front when you left the hotel,' he said, 'and I followed you to that nightclub. It cost me five bucks for one drink, five bucks and taxi fare to write that note.' He suddenly pulled the girl up out of her chair and into his arms.

'This is pretty damned unplanned,' Farland said.

'I got to have half an hour with Marie. We've got to settle some things,' Tom said peremptorily. 'I'm sorry I was so abrupt.' He held out the hand that swept things off mantelpieces. He had a quick, firm grip. 'I haven't got any plans, except to get her away from that monkey,' he said.

'The law is on his side, of course,' Farland put in, 'and the church and all that sort of thing.' The girl had freed herself and sat down again, and Tom resumed his pacing.

'Do you know the grip?' Farland asked her suddenly. 'I think it may be mine. Don't hit me,' he said to the young man.

'Tom threw his pledge pin across the room at a chapter meeting, I think they call it,' the girl said.

'Somebody said something,' Tom snarled.

Farland nodded. 'People have a way of doing that,' he said. 'Human failing.' He held out his right hand to the girl and she gave him the grip. 'Now I do *this*,' he said, pressing her wrist. 'And I do *this*,' she said, returning the pressure. Each then pressed the other's thumb.

'Don't you wiggle your ears, for crissake?' Tom snarled.

'Brother Endicott,' Farland sighed, 'shake hands with Brother Farland. Pennsylvania Gamma.' He picked up the unopened bottle of bourbon and the ice bucket. 'I think I can promise you your half hour undisturbed,' he said. 'God's whisky and the grip ought to do it, and besides, I know the words of "Back in Your Own back Yard." I also know the "Darling" song.'

'God,' said Marie Endicott.

Tom stopped pacing and looked at Farland. 'Damned white of you,' he said, 'but I don't know why you're doing it.'

'Lady in distress,' Farland said. 'Cry for help in the night. I don't know much about drums, but I can talk about Brother Hunk Elliot.'

'Ohio Gamma,' said Mrs Endicott bleakly. 'Greatest by God halfback that ever lugged a football, even if he did beat Wisconsin three straight years. Crazy Legs and the Horse don't belong to Boopa Doopa Chi, so they don't rate with Brother Elliot.'

'The protocol of fraternity is extremely complicated and uninteresting,' Farland said.

'Nuts,' snapped Tom, who had begun to crack his knuckles. 'Why doesn't that goddam racket stop?' He suddenly leaped at the open window of the salon and shouted into the night, 'Cut down that goddam noise!'

'Do you want everybody *in* here?' the girl asked nervously.

'I don't see why I shouldn't go down there myself and bust him a couple,' he said. 'I don't see why you had to marry him anyway. Nobody in her right mind would marry a man old enough to be her father, and live in Milwaukee.' He whirled and stared at Farland. 'I don't see what you're getting out of this,' he said, 'acting like her fairy godfather or somebody.'

'I—' Farland began, but Mrs Endicott cut in on him. There was a new storm in her eyes. 'He's done more for me in one night than you have in two years!' she said. 'You never wrote, and when you did, nobody could read it, the way you write. How do I know who you were running around with in Tacoma? You're not really in love with me, you just want something somebody else has got.' Farland tried to get in on it again, but Tom Gregg gave him a little push and turned to the girl again.

'It wasn't Tacoma,' he said. 'You didn't even bother to find out what camp I was at.'

'Seattle, then,' she said. 'Fort Lawton. And everybody else got married. I know ten girls who went to camp with their husbands, and three of them were in Tacoma.'

'We couldn't get married on nothing,' he said. 'I happen to have a job now, a good job.'

'Everybody else got married on nothing,' she said.

'I'm not everybody else!' he yelled. 'I'm not just anybody else, either. "Miss Withrow, I want you to meet Mr Endicott." "How do you do, Miss Withrow. Will you marry me?" "Sure, why not? I think I'm engaged to a guy named Tacoma or something, but that's okay."'

'I'll hit you, I really will!' cried the former Miss Withrow.

Farland hastily put the bottle and the ice bucket on the floor and stepped between them. 'I'm not anybody's fairy godfather,' he said. 'I'm just an innocent bystander. I was about to go to bed when all this hell broke loose, and I'll be damned if I'm going down to that room and sing with a lot of big fat emblem makers if you're going to spend your time fighting.' His voice was pitched even louder than theirs. The telephone rang. Farland picked up the receiver and listened for three seconds to a voice on the other end speaking in French. 'It's the Fourth of July!' he yelled and slammed down the receiver.

'I'm sorry about this,' Tom said. 'I'm willing to talk it over rationally if she is. I got to fly back to work day after tomorrow.'

'Oh, sure,' said Marie.

'I don't usually lose my temper,' Farland apologised, 'but I'm stuck in a book I'm writing, and it makes me jumpy.' He picked up the bottle and the ice bucket again. 'I'll give you until four o'clock,' he said. 'I'll knock four times, with an interval after the third.'

'You probably haven't got your key,' Marie said. She spied it, put it in Farland's pocket, and kissed him on the forehead.

'Do you have to keep doing that?' Tom shouted.

'I haven't *been* doing that,' Marie said.

'Please!' Farland said. 'I'm tossing her aside like a broken doll, anyway.' He grinned. 'How in hell can I open this door with my arms loaded?' Marie crossed over and opened the door for him. 'For God's sake, don't kiss me again,' he whispered, 'and stop fighting and get something worked out.' He raised his voice and spoke to both of them. 'Goodnight,' he said, 'and shut up.' He stepped out into the hall and the girl in the green dress quietly closed the door after him . . .

A short, heavy-set man in his middle forties opened the door, and seemed to block the way aggressively until he caught sight of the American face of the visitor and the things he was carrying. 'I heard the Yankee Doodle sounds,' Farland told him, and introduced himself. 'I thought maybe you needed reinforcements.' The room exploded into American sounds, as if the newcomer had dropped a lighted match in a box of fireworks. Somebody took the bourbon from him and somebody else the ice bucket. 'My God, it's real ice!' someone said, and 'Brother, you've saved our lives!'

'An American shouldn't spend this night alone,' Farland said above the hubbub. The biggest man in the room, who wore no coat or tie, but on whose vest a fraternity pin gleamed, held out his hand in three parts. Farland gave him the full-dress grip. 'Ed Endicott, Wisconsin Alpha!' bawled the big man.

'Pennsylvania Gamma,' Farland said.

'For crissake, it's a small world!' Endicott said. 'Rip, shake hands with Brother Farland, give him the old grip. Brother Morgan and I belong to the same chapter. Wisconsin Alpha has two national presidents to its credit,' he told Farland, 'and I was one of them, if I do say so myself. These other poor guys took the wrong pins, but they're okay.' He managed somehow to get his right arm around the shoulders of both the other men in the room. 'This is Sam Winterhorn, Phi Gam from Illinois, and this is Red Perry, also Illini – Red's a Phi Psi. Maybe you heard us doing "Fiji Honeymoon" and "When DKE Has Gone to Hell." Put 'er there again, fella.'

Farland was glad when he was finally given a glass to hold instead of a man's right hand. 'Here's to all the brothers, whatever sky's above 'em,' Endicott said, clinking his glass against Farland's He took a great gulp of his drink, and it seemed to Farland that his face brightened like a full moon coming out from behind a cloud. 'Endicott is a curly wolf this night, Guy, and you can write that home to your loved ones!' he roared. 'Endicott is going to shake hands with the pearly-fingered dawn this day. Endicott is going to ring all the bells and blow all the whistles in hell. Any frog that don't like it can bury his head in the Tooleries.' Farland managed to get out part of a word, but Brother Endicott trampled on it. 'The girls have gone to bed,' he said. 'Wish you could meet Marie, but we'll be around a couple of more days. Marie's Eastern women's college, but Brenda – that's my first wife – was a Kappa. So's Ellen Morgan, Rip's wife. Brenda hated drums. I got the greatest little drum collection in the world, Guy. Once, when a gang of us got up a storm in my house – this was six-seven years ago – damned if Brenda didn't call the cops! One of them turned out to be real mean with the sticks, but the other guy was a surly bastard. I tried to give him the grip, and he got sore as hell. Don't ever try to give a cop the grip, Guy. They think you're queer. Sons-of-bitches never get through high school.'

Farland put on his fixed grin as Endicott rambled on, moving among the disarranged chairs like a truck. He paused in front of one in which Brother Morgan now lay back relaxed, with his eyes closed. 'Judas Priest, our tenor's conking out,' he said.

"Way,' mumbled Morgan sleepily.

'Let him sleep,' said the man named Perry. 'What the hell, we still got a quartet. Anyway, what good's a sleepy tenor unless you're doing "Sleepy Time Gal"?'

'"Sleepy Time Gal!"' bawled Endicott, and he suddenly started in the middle of the old song, biting a great hunk out of the lyric. The phone rang, and Endicott smote the night with a bathroom word and jerked up the receiver. 'Yeah?' he began truculently, and, as the voice at the other end began protesting in French, he said to the revellers, 'It's one of them quoi-quois.' He winked heavily at Farland and addressed the transmitter. 'Parlez-vous la langue de Dieu?' he asked. Farland realized he had been rehearsing the question quite a while. 'Bien, then,' Endicott went on. 'You people ought to be celebrating, too. If we hadn't let Lafayette fight on our side, he would have gone to the goddam guillotine. The way it was, even Napoleon didn't dare lay a hand on him. They cut the head off Rabelais and Danton, but they couldn't touch Lafayette, and that's on account of the good old Thirteen States.' The person at the other end had apparently hung up, but Endicott went on with his act. 'Get yourselves a bottle of grenadine and a pack of cubebs and raise a little hell for Lafayette,' he said, and hung up.

'Not Rabelais,' Farland couldn't help saying. 'Robespierre.'

'Or old Roquefort!' Endicott bawled. 'They all sound like cheese to me, rich old framboise, and they all look alike. Let's hit the "Darling" song again.'

They got through 'Three O'Clock in the Morning' and 'Linger Awhile' and 'Over There' and 'Yankee Doodle Dandy' and 'You're the B-E-S-T Best' and by that time it was ten minutes after four. 'Don't keep looking at your Benrus,' Endicott told Farland. 'Nobody's going anywhere. What the hell, we've got all day.' Rip Morgan's troubled unconscious greeted this with a faint moaning sound. Farland's tone grew firm and terminal, and the Illinois men joined him and began the final round of handshakes. Farland picked up the ice bucket, which had been empty for some time now, and started for the door.

'We'll all meet in the bar downstairs at six,' Endicott commanded. 'Be there!' The two departing Americans said they would be there. 'I'm going to stay stiff till they pour me on the plane,' Endicott went on. Farland's hand felt full of fingers after he had shaken hands again with the Illinois men and they had gone. Brother Endicott, he felt sure, would have his hands full for at least fifteen minutes, putting Brother Morgan to bed . . .

Farland rapped on the door of his suite three times, paused, and rapped again. There was no response, and he unlocked the door and went in. All the lights in the sitting room were out except one, and he turned it off and began undressing before he reached the bedroom. The battle of the Paris night still went on, and it seemed louder than ever. Farland put on the bottom of his pyjamas, couldn't find the top, said, 'The hell with it,' and went into the bathroom and brushed his teeth. 'Everything happens to you,' he sneered at the man in the mirror. 'What's the matter, don't you know how to duck any more?'

He was about to throw himself on his bed when he noticed the note on his pillow. It read simply, 'You are the B-E-S-T Best,' and it was signed, obviously in Mrs Endicott's handwriting, 'Tom and Marie.' In spite of the noise and his still tingling right hand, Farland fell asleep. When he woke up, he picked up the telephone and called the *renseignement* desk. He looked at his watch. It was nine-thirty-five. 'I want to get a plane out of here for Rome this afternoon,' he said when the information desk answered. 'A single seat. And I don't care what line. There is just one thing. It has *got* to leave before six o'clock.'